TOP COPS:

Those Who Dare to Care

Based on Stories by

PAM PROCTOR
&
JOHN G. ROGERS

With an Introduction and Epilogue by

Craig W. Floyd

POTOMAC PUBLISHING, 1991

The stories contained in this book are based on articles by Pam Proctor and John G. Rogers that originally appeared in PARADE Magazine.

Cover Photo: Paul McIver.

Cover Art: Jon Milburn.

Printed in the United States of America.

TABLE OF CONTENTS

ACKNOWLEDGMENTS

On behalf of the National Law Enforcement Officers Memorial Fund, I wish to thank the many individuals who made this book possible, including Larry Smith, Managing Editor, PARADE Magazine, who so kindly assisted the Memorial Fund in reprinting the wonderful articles that have appeared in that magazine since 1966, featuring the officers who received PARADE/ International Association of Chiefs of Police annual "Police Officer of the Year" awards. Thanks are also due to Pam Proctor and John G. Rogers, who wrote the PARADE articles.

Most of all, however, I wish to thank the law enforcement officers who appear in these pages, not only for allowing us to tell their stories once again, but also and especially for their remarkable courage and commitment in service to their communities.

—Craig W. Floyd, Chairman
National Law Enforcement
Officers Memorial Fund

DEDICATION

This book is dedicated to the thousands of law enforcement officers who have served their communities and their nation without concern for their own safety, to the thousands serving today, and to those who will serve us in the future, as well as to the families of those who gave their lives in the line of duty. For all you have done to serve and to protect, the National Law Enforcement Officers Memorial Fund and its hundreds of thousands of citizen supporters salute you.

INTRODUCTION

They walk *toward* danger, while the rest of us run from it. *Toward* knives and guns, burning cars and ticking bombs, landslides, earthquakes, and floods.

In return for their efforts, they're called "pigs." "The fuzz." And many other names that aren't fit to print.

They have been reviled by an ungrateful society. Killed and wounded by ruthless, vicious criminals. And forgotten by a public that just didn't seem to care.

I hope this book will help to change all of that.

As Chairman of the National Law Enforcement Officers Memorial Fund, I am proud to represent an organization supported by some 700,000 Americans who do care about the sacrifices made by our nation's police officers. They care so much, in fact, that they have made sacrifices of their own—financial sacrifices—in order to build a memorial to honor our fallen law enforcement heroes.

These law-abiding Americans believe the time has come to recognize law enforcement officers, just as we pay our respects to our military heroes. They—and I—believe that the 12,500 officers who have died in the line of duty since 1794 deserve a fitting tribute in the heart of our nation's capital, Washington, D.C.

In 1985, Congress agreed, and authorized the National Law Enforcement Officers Memorial to be built. Congress also stipulated that this Memorial was to be built by the dimes and dollars sent in by ordinary American citizens— that not one penny of government money could be used in its planning or construction.

The National Law Enforcement Officers Memorial Fund gladly took up the challenge. Slowly but surely, we grew from an organization made up of just a few stalwarts, mostly individuals within the law enforcement "family," to a mighty coalition of caring individuals who want to fulfill their obligation to the law enforcement officers who make life safe for the rest of us.

And, slowly but surely, we have overcome major obstacles, gaining approval for the site we hoped to build on, Judiciary Square, near the U.S. Capitol, the Mall, and Washington's other great memorials. We worked laboriously through the "red tape" presented by government commissions. We painstakingly created a plan for our Memorial—a monument that would be second to none, because our officers deserve the very best.

The Memorial will feature two 300-foot marble walls on which the names of our fallen heroes will be engraved . . . a reflecting pool. . .and a tree-lined Pathway of Remembrance in a serene, park-like setting, right in the middle of America's bustling capital city.

Here—at last—the families of officers who died in the line of duty can come to remember and to heal. All Americans who understand the sacrifices of law enforcement officers can and will come, to pay tribute to those who have died, to those who have sustained injuries, and to those who serve today.

This long-overdue Memorial will not only honor those who have made the ultimate sacrifice. It will also represent the basic decency of the American people, the individuals who believe in law and order, peace and freedom—the American way.

Now, after seven long years of hard work and struggle, we are nearing the time when at last we will be able to say, "It is done—the debt of honor has been repaid."

But this Memorial will not be finished without the continued financial support of the American people. As this book goes to press, an additional $2.5 million must be raised in order to complete construction and to ensure the Memorial's future through a maintenance endowment— because, tragically, we know that more names will have to be added to its handsome marble walls, as more officers lay down their lives in service to community and to country.

This book has been created with two aims in mind. First, the Memorial Fund wishes to honor those extraordinary law enforcement officers who have been singled out for recognition by the PARADE/International Association of Chiefs of Police awards since 1966. We want to bring their accomplishments to light for you and for thousands of others who may not know about them.

Second, we hope to raise the remaining funds needed to build and endow the Memorial by placing this book in the hands of caring Americans like you. Once you read just one of the stories in this book, I believe you will want to help us complete the Memorial. And I hope you will do so by sending a generous contribution to the National Law Enforcement Officers Memorial Fund just as soon as you possibly can.

If you're one of the people who would never call a police officer a "pig," then I know you'll enjoy TOP COPS. It will refresh and inspire you. You'll read stories of great heroism. You'll meet men and women who call themselves "ordinary cops"—and you'll know that they're anything but!

CHAPTER 1

THE MEN WHO SAVED
PRESIDENT REAGAN'S LIFE

They are special policemen, fine-tuned for a single purpose: to protect the President. Self-preservation—a powerful instinct in most of us—is suppressed. "It's the result of training," says Secret Service Agent Tim McCarthy, who blocked a bullet with his body instead of ducking. "The point is to drill the reaction into you."

The hours of training paid off on March 30, 1981, when four Secret Service men, working together as a team, saved President Reagan's life. For their achievement, these men—Special Agent Dennis V.N. McCarthy, Special Agent Timothy J. McCarthy, Special Agent in Charge Jerry S. Parr, and Assistant to the Special Agent in Charge Raymond A. Shaddick—received the 16th annual Police Service Award given by PARADE and the International Association of Chiefs of Police (IACP).

The events of that March afternoon are still familiar to most Americans. The President was leaving the Washington Hilton Hotel via the VIP exit. He turned to wave to a small group of onlookers when six shots rang out, wounding the President, press secretary James S. Brady, Agent Timothy McCarthy, and a Washington, D.C., policeman, Thomas K. Delahanty. A 25-year-old drifter named John W. Hinckley, Jr. was arrested for allegedly trying to assassinate the President.

Dennis McCarthy, 46, part of the Secret Service intelligence team, had left the hotel ahead of the President to scan the crowd of 25 or 30 cameramen and bystanders. As he tells it: "I heard people saying, 'Mr. President.

Over here, Mr. President.' And about that time—pop!—the first round went off. I had a feeling of panic because I couldn't see the gun.

"After the second shot, I saw the hands and the gun coming out of the crowd, and I sort of just dove. I don't remember leaving the ground—just going through the air and seeing him in a crouch position. I came down on top of him. I put my arm around his head and reached for his gun, and we went down. Then everybody started piling on. I reached around and got my handcuffs out. He didn't struggle. I knew we had to get him out of there fast. I kept thinking, 'We have to keep him alive.'"

Tim McCarthy (no relation to Dennis), a member of the White House detail that moved with the President, had just opened the door of the heavily armored limousine when the first shot rang out. "I didn't know exactly where it came from," he says, "but I was looking. The adrenaline was pumping, but fear never entered into it. There was only time to react. I turned to put myself between the potential threat and the President.

"I believe it was the third shot that got me. There was that initial thud and extremely sharp pain. I could feel the bullet going in through the chest and down through the liver. I tried to remain as calm as I could. That was based on training: 'Remain calm so you don't go into shock.' In spite of the pain, I was still totally lucid. I thought I was fairly stable and that it was best to remain [on his right side] until someone got to me."

Jerry Parr, 51, the top man on the detail, and his assistant, Ray Shaddick, 37, had moved out of the hotel behind the President. At the first shot, they shifted into action. "I knew where the limousine's open door was," says Parr, "and that we had to get behind it. I moved to the President's left and grabbed him by the upper left shoulder. My right hand went around his waist, and I drove my shoulder into him forward and down. Shaddick came from the rear. He got his hand on the small of my back and part of the President's, and we both shoved him rapidly into the car."

Parr ended up on top of the President, who hit his chest on the hump on the car's rear floor. Shaddick saw their feet dangling out, shoved them into the car and slammed the door. "I told [driver] Drew Unrue to move out," says Parr. The President said, 'I think you really hurt my ribs when you came down.'"

Parr pushed the President into a seated position. "Next," he relates, "was to find out if the President was injured. I opened up his coat and ran my hands up under his arms and on his back, bent him over and looked at his head. I could find no evidence of a wound."

He radioed to Ray Shaddick in the follow-up car that they were heading for the White House. "Almost within four or five seconds of that," says Parr, "he started to complain of difficulty in breathing. He was developing a pallor, and he started coughing up bright red blood. I knew he had a lung injury. I told the President, 'We're going to the hospital.'

"He and I talked the whole time. I told him he was going to be OK. He was very alert and concerned. But he really maintained his dignity and cool."

Within three minutes, they were at George Washington University Hospital, and Parr ordered the waiting agents to set up a protective perimeter around the

President. "He started out of the car," says Parr, "and there was sort of something that was unsaid: 'I am going to walk. Presidents walk.'"

Parr and other agents guided President Reagan into the hospital, lifted him onto a trolley and followed him into the operating room. It was 11 p.m. when Parr went home to get some rest.

In protecting the President, each agent has a precise role. Ray Shaddick was the team's "whip"—the second in command who controlled the movements of the Presidential entourage through a tiny radio on his wrist. When he learned in the hospital that the President had been wounded, he reacted with anger. "I was mad at myself—mad that the assailant was so lucky," he says. "Knowing how he was shot irritated me even more."

The President apparently was shot, says Shaddick, when he was being pushed into the limousine. In that split second, a bullet ricocheted off the car and through the vertical gap between the hinges of the open door. "It was a fluke," he insists, adding that there is "nothing at all" he would have done differently that day.

Perhaps the agent whose relationship with the President was most dramatically affected on March 30 was Tim McCarthy, the man who blocked the bullet. Before the assassination attempt, says McCarthy, "the President probably recognized my face—but I don't think he knew my name."

These days, he said, President Reagan makes a point of asking how he's doing, and Mrs. Reagan treats him with special affection. Recently, though, the First Lady walked right past him without a word and got on an elevator. "All of a sudden," says McCarthy, "she came rushing out of the elevator and put her arms around me. 'I didn't see you,' she said. 'You know, I'm near-sighted.'"

Three months after the shooting, McCarthy was back on the job and was sent out to guard the President along with Jerry Parr. "I was in the same position as on the day of the shooting," says McCarthy, "opening the door of the limousine and standing there. I thought, 'Here we go again.'"

But things weren't quite the same. Now he wears a bulletproof vest. His wife insists on it.

Also honored by PARADE and the IACP was Officer Thomas K. Delahanty, of Washington D.C.'s Metropolitan Police Department, Washington, D.C. Assigned to a security detail at the Washington Hilton that day, he was struck by a bullet intended for the President. Even while being felled, he was drawing his revolver. Officer Delahanty received Honorable Mention in the 1981 awards.

An Update on the Men Who Saved the President

Jerry Parr is now a pastor and counselor at Potter's House, a part of the Church of the Savior in Washington, D.C. He also does consulting in the security business. "I guess you'd say I'm one of George Bush's 'thousand points of light,'" Parr told PARADE recently. "I still have my hand in a little counseling with the homeless. I have a master's in pastoral counseling from Loyola, and a Doctor of Humane letters from Eureka."

Parr left the Secret Service in February 1985 as assistant director for protective research. "I left the Presidential Detail in 1982. At the time, I was getting a master's degree part time. For 18 months, I was vice president of Penn Central Security Company. But I discovered I wasn't into the private sector."

Parr sees a link between his life in law enforcement and his work today. "What I discovered in my life in the Secret Service is that basically I'm a rescuer. I'm still doing it." Parr works with the homeless, addicts, and alcoholics on a daily basis.

"People ask me about the incident all the time," he told PARADE. It was a great event of my life. But what built up to it was thousands of hours of doing mundane things."

Raymond Shaddick is still with the Secret Service. "In 1981, I left Presidential protection and went to Honolulu, where I was the Agent in Charge. From there, I went back to Presidential protection in March 1985, as Agent in Charge. Then I went through a transition. I was AIC until March 1990. Now, I'm deputy assistant director for protective operations in headquarters. I oversee all of the protection in the Secret Service, including the President, Vice President and Foreign dignitaries."

Shaddick says President Bush and Vice President Quayle keep his agency busy. "This twosome is much more active in terms of travel. George Bush and Dan Quayle have been the most active twosome we've ever had. We have a President who's about as active as the Vice President. It puts extra pressures on the Secret Service—our resources, our manpower."

Shaddick updated PARADE on the two other officers who received the Policemen of the Year Award in 1981. "Dennis McCarthy wrote a book and went into the private sector. Tim McCarthy is now Assistant Agent in charge of the Chicago office."

Ray Shaddick says the memory of the assassination attempt never leaves: "You always think about it. Right after it happened, everything's hush-hush. As time goes on, you talk about the details, and about what happened at the hospital. I hope it never happens again." All of America joins this courageous officer in the hope that this nation has suffered its last Presidential assassination attempt, and we salute the Secret Service Agents who stand ever ready to put themselves between our national leaders and a bullet.

CHAPTER 2

A SALUTE TO A "ROAD WARRIOR"

The average police officer spends a lot of time dealing with cars and drivers, from issuing citations for driving while intoxicated to attending to accident victims, some of the bloodiest and most dangerous work in the cop's routine. According to the National Highway Traffic Safety Administration, 45,555 Americans died in auto accidents in 1989 and another 3,356,000 were injured.

These tragic numbers would be even higher if it were not for the dedicated efforts of law enforcement officers nationwide, whose work in safety and traffic patrol, as well as on the scenes of accidents, has been recognized many times by the PARADE/IACP awards.

But among this cadre of heroes, one officer—nicknamed the "Road Warrior" by admiring colleagues—stands out for a single act of valor most of us cannot even conceive of.

Sgt. Kenneth Pollock of the Maryland State Police saw a car careening down the wrong side of a highway at more than 90 miles an hour, heading directly toward a van carrying a couple and their newborn daughter. In a desperate effort to save the young family from certain death, he gunned his unmarked police car, made a sharp right turn in front of the van, and stopped directly in the path of the oncoming vehicle.

Miraculously, the undercover cop survived. And a few months later, he received the 22nd annual Police Officer of the Year Award, given by PARADE and the International Association of Chiefs of Police.

Moments before the speeding car crashed into him,

though, Pollock wasn't feeling so heroic. A 19-year veteran who had been a trooper before joining the narcotics division five years before, Pollock had had his fill of traffic accidents. To die like this—ignominiously splattered on the road, after living through four shootouts and numerous drug busts—seemed sadly ironic to him.

He was haunted too by the memory of another accident, seven years before, which had taken the life of his own 16-year-old son, Jeffrey. The teenager, whom Pollock had raised after a divorce, had been fatally injured when the motorcycle on which he was a passenger struck a curb and threw him into a telephone pole.

The boy died minutes later on the street, in Pollock's arms.

In the months following Jeffrey's death, Pollock would shake uncontrollably at the sight of an auto accident. Eventually, he transferred to the narcotics division.

Despite his aversion to the road, however, Pollock didn't hesitate to act on March 23, 1987, when his radio crackled with the report of a high-speed chase down Interstate 70 near Baltimore. Two police cars were pursuing a vehicle being driven at speeds up to 100 miles per hour by a woman later described by police as depressed and panic-stricken, and they were calling for help.

"She's crossed the median strip—airborne—and now she's headed eastbound in the westbound lane," a trooper called over the radio.

Since no marked police cars were in his area, Pollock knew that he had to break his cover and stop traffic— fast. What he didn't know was that he had only five minutes to halt all westbound traffic to avert disaster.

He already was in the westbound lane. He jumped out of his car, held up his badge and motioned the cars to stop. The trouble was—with his scruffy undercover look—he seemed more like a deranged man than a state trooper.

Luckily, a tractor-trailer driver was the first to respond, and others followed. Pollock raced between the cars, shouting at people to get out and stand on the grassy shoulder of the road, as far from the highway as possible.

Most got the message. But David Cannon, 32, his wife Laura, 31, and their infant daughter, Caitlin, remained in their van instead of getting out. Sergeant Pollock could see that they were at the very head of the line of parked cars—sitting ducks for the speeding auto.

In the few seconds remaining before the rampaging car came into view, Pollock jumped into his car, put on his seat belt and zigzagged around the parked vehicles, planning to place his car in front of the van like a barricade—and then get out. But there was no time to escape. He looked ahead and "there she was," he recalled. The runaway car was headed right for the van.

As Pollock came up on the van's left and veered to the right, his car was hit immediately on the driver's side.

"It sounded like a cannon going off," said Pollock, who was bounced to the other side of his car and back, then thrown headfirst into the windshield. He heard a second crash as the woman plowed next into a parked Cadillac before coming to a stop.

David Cannon jumped out to check Pollock's car. "I thought I was going to see pieces of him," he recalled.

Instead he helped a dazed Pollock through the car window. The sergeant had a broken nose, a concussion, and a slipped disk.

As Cannon looked around at the devastation—three cars smashed and several people injured, but no fatalities—he sensed, he said, the hand of God at work in Pollock's action. "I know it sounds funny," said Cannon, a devout Pentecostal from Middletown, Maryland, "but I believe he was an angel. God knew exactly where to put him."

Pollock's buddies, however, have brought him down to earth by dubbing him "Road Warrior." Still, the hero cop was quick to point out that it wasn't macho heroics—but a seat belt—that saved him. He's so insistent on safety that when he presented his teenage daughter, Pam, with a car, he made her sign a contract promising always to buckle up.

Pollock retired in October 1989 because of his injuries. "The doctors and State Police doctors thought that with the type of injuries I had, I could never come back as a trooper," Pollock said. "It kind of broke my heart a little bit, but that's the way it goes. I get a lot of migraine headaches, and I have a problem with short-term memory. 'Post-trauma' is what my neurosurgeon said. It can last from two to five years or forever. And I have a slipped disk. My nose—I finally had plastic surgery done on that. It was broken in three places."

Today Pollock works as a private investigator. "We do all types of investigations for insurance companies and also for lawyers. Our cases range from reconstruction of accidents to domestic cases. Insurance fraud, background investigations on people. Workman's comp cases."

He also takes joy in spending time with his second wife, Linda, and their 2-year-old son, Nicholas. But he admits he would put his life on the line again. His response to the accident, he says, was not the trained instinct of a cop, but the deliberate decision of a man who was compelled by his own tragedy to spare others.

Pollock keeps in touch with the Cannon family. "I call the Cannons every once in a while—mainly at Christmas. They're doing fine. Every now and then I stop and think about the kid. I'm just so pleased that these people didn't have to suffer the horror that I went through by losing a child," he says. "Maybe that was my purpose in life—to save this little baby."

Pollock's heroic deed was re-enacted on the "Rescue 911" television show. "Today, he says, the Maryland State Police shows the "911" videotape to all recruit classes. It's something that every young buck trooper knows about. When I'm introduced, they all know who I am. They look at me with wide eyes. 'There's the old dinosaur,' they'll say."

But Pollock's greatest reward, he says, is that his son Jeffrey would have been bursting with pride.

"I know exactly what he would have said," says Pollock, with a wistful smile: 'Old man, you did a helluva job.'"

Other "road warriors" recognized for their heroism by PARADE/IACP include:

Officer William Martin, San Bruna, California, Honorable Mention, 1967.

A rookie, Martin was directing traffic at a busy corner near a railroad crossing when a station wagon stalled on the tracks as a train approached. Martin pulled four children and a baby out of the car. He had the entire party safe when the woman driver ran back to get her purse as the train struck. She was fatally injured.

Patrolman Richard L. Viecelli, Detroit, Michigan, Honorable Mention, 1968.

Viecelli saw a truck capsize on the Ford Freeway. The driver was injured and pinned in the cab. Though the truck teetered on a guard rail, Viecelli risked a 35-foot fall, squeezed into the cab and aided the driver for five and one-half hours until both were rescued.

Trooper Grady W. Smith, Baton Rouge, Louisiana, Honorable Mention, 1969.

While two motorists were changing tires, Smith saw another approaching erratically. At risk of his own life, Smith dived forward, shoving the motorists to safety. The resulting crash threw Smith through the air and knocked him unconscious, severely bruising the trooper.

Officer William O'Brien, St. Paul, Minnesota, Honorable Mention, 1969.

This state highway patrol officer was first on the scene when a car hit the side of a freight train. Dragged along the tracks under a box car, the auto caught fire. O'Brien crawled into this moving holocaust and pulled out the only survivor. Two other passengers perished.

Officer Edward Gamble, California Highway Patrol, Honorable Mention, 1971.

Gamble saw a dune buggy in a California recreation

area skid, roll over, and burst into flames, with the driver and a passenger strapped into place. Gamble dashed into the flames and managed to extricate one. The other died. Badly burned, Gamble spent a week in a hospital.

Trooper Alan J. Loman, Wisconsin State Patrol, Honorable Mention, 1972.

Loman, while on patrol, came upon a blazing car. The owner suddenly made a break for the auto, shouting that he had to recover $100. The gas tank "has to explode any second now," a spectator yelled. Loman ran to deter the owner, held on, and suffered major burns in the explosion.

Trooper Cornel B. Piebani, New Jersey State Police, Honorable Mention, 1974.

Trooper Piebani was first on the scene of a pile-up on the fog-shrouded New Jersey Turnpike in which nine were killed and 42 injured. Ignoring his own safety, he crawled into the blazing tangle of trucks and cars, hauling out victims. At one point a burning trailer's fuel supply exploded, throwing him to the side of the road, but he returned, his uniform singed and torn. Although he was at the point of collapse from exhaustion, he kept on working until other rescuers arrived, and then he helped direct their operations from his squad car.

Officer Richard A. Deriso, U.S. Park Police, Honorable Mention, 1987.

As a small car was being swept away by torrential floods on a Washington, D.C., roadway, Deriso leapt into the raging waters to save the two terrified occupants.

Moments before the car sank, he pulled the two through the car window to safety.

Detective Richard E. Kaufman, Nassau County, New York Police Department, Honorable Mention, 1988.

Kaufman pulled an unconscious passenger through the rear window of a flaming car and was inside, trying to free the driver, when firemen arrived. Both victims are recovering.

Cpl. Michael A. Cooper, Missouri State Highway Patrol, Honorable Mention, 1989.

Cooper rescued the driver who had outrun him in a high speed chase when the man's car hit a tree and burst into flames. Moments after Cooper had freed the unconscious driver, who was wedged in the vehicle with his clothes on fire, shotgun shells in the car's glove compartment began exploding.

These stories are representative of the thousands of rescues performed by law enforcement officers all across America. But we must also remember that hundreds of officers die in auto accidents which occur as they pursue dangerous criminals or race to the scene of a crime. The National Law Enforcement Officers Memorial will include their names, too, as fallen heroes who gave their lives for their country.

CHAPTER 3

THE ULTIMATE SACRIFICE

As an instructor at the FBI Academy in Quantico, Special Agent Ed Mireles taught new agents some tough lessons.

"This is a profession where you have to be truly dedicated to the job, the work, the mission. You have to truly believe you are doing something right, you are serving the public, and you are serving the community. You also have to understand that this type of job can get you killed. If you're afraid of getting killed, injured, disfigured, or maimed, this is not the right place for you."

Nobody knows this hard truth better than law enforcement officers who have seen their partners or fellow officers wounded or killed in the line of duty. Among the officers honored by the PARADE/IACP awards since 1966, many have learned these lessons in the too-real classroom of the streets.

Take Laurine Venable, for example, an officer with the Philadelphia Police Department, who chased the slayer of her partner, Officer Dan Gleason, and—after a running gun battle—wounded and arrested the suspect. For her bravery under fire, Officer Venable received an Honorable Mention Award from PARADE/IACP in 1986.

And 1989 Honorable Mention winner, Officer Greg Armstrong of the Tallahassee, Florida Police Department, faced a similar situation as a rookie cop. When a shootout left his backup officer dead, Greg Armstrong took on three heavily armed escaped convicts, seriously wounding all three while reloading twice and calling for aid. Armstrong was just one month out of police training.

Or consider the heroic actions of 1989's Police Officer of the Year Gregory Jaglowski, who, like Officer Venable, did his utmost to try to save his partner's life. Though Officer Irma Ruiz died, Jaglowski continued the battle without her—and prevented an all-out massacre in a Chicago school.

That terrible day began like any other for Ruiz and Jaglowski, partners on the Chicago Police Department for nearly four years. But it soon became a nightmare in which Greg Jaglowski, wounded in the leg by a deranged gunman who had just slain three persons—staggered toward the school where the killer had fled. He heard gunfire. His partner was in there, along with nearly 200 children and teachers. In the moments that followed, Jaglowski killed the gunman and thereby saved perhaps dozens of lives.

"Had it not been for Greg," said Bernard Karlin, principal of the Moses Montefiore School, where the incident took place, "it could have been a massacre. We owe him our lives."

Chicago Police Superintendent LeRoy Martin concurred: "Anybody who crossed the assailant's path that day was going to get shot and killed. He had already killed innocent people, two in an auto-parts store and one of the engineers at the school. He was hell-bent on destruction."

Greg Jaglowski's story is also the story of a partnership between two officers.

"Greg was a shining example of what a policeman should be," said Karlin, who worked closely with

Jaglowski and Ruiz during their four years together as school patrol officers. "He treated all the kids much the way he treated his own daughter," said Sgt. Tom Fuller, a police supervisor.

Jaglowski's partner was like a mother figure. With four children of her own at home, Irma Ruiz "knew exactly what to say to kids," said Victor Zapatka, a guidance counselor at Montefiore.

Typical was the time Ruiz and Jaglowski came upon a woman scolding her 8-year-old son. "If you're not good," the woman warned the boy, "these policemen will put you in jail."

"Oh, I'd never put you in jail," replied Ruiz, looking warmly at the child. "I know you're too good a boy."

On September 22, 1988, Montefiore reported that a student had assaulted a teacher, but by the time Ruiz and Jaglowski got there, the boy had gone home. Then came the report of shots. Jaglowski was first out the door. A bullet hit him in the leg, knocking him down. He dove for cover as the gunman raced into the school.

"I thought Irma had gone for cover," said Jaglowski. "I hoped she had."

As a shot rang out, Jaglowski headed back inside the school, dazed and bleeding from his wound. There, in a pool of blood, lay his partner. Irma had been shot once in the chest. She was dead at age 40. The gunman, later identified as Clemmie Henderson, had ducked into the school library to reload. As Jaglowski looked up, he came out shooting from only a few feet away.

"It looked like fire coming out of his gun," recalled Jaglowski. "It was like slow motion; I could almost feel the bullets going by me."

The cop fired back, trading bullets with the gunman, who shot him in his other leg, severing an artery. Jaglowski kept pumping rounds into the man.

Nothing seemed to stop the gunman. But with his last bullet, Jaglowski finally dropped Henderson, a jobless neighborhood figure with a history of erratic behavior. In his blood and urine, according to the medical examiner, were traces of the drug PCP, also known as angel dust.

For Jaglowski, a new battle was just beginning.

"Sometimes I still can't believe that Irma is dead," said the police veteran. "You get angry when you think about these things. Sometimes it bothers me why God would take someone like that."

"His wounds are healing," said Jaglowski's wife, Diana. "He's walking and he's functioning. But what's rough is the mental part of it—losing Irma and seeing her kids not having a mother and her husband not having a wife."

Jaglowski could have remained outside the school, tending his own wounds and calling for help, said Commander Ettore DiVito, his chief in the Youth division. "But the fact that he did go back into the school—that's what separates a hero from just a good, solid police officer."

Today, Gregory Jaglowski accepts such accolades with a self-effacing smile and then sets the record straight.

"Remember Irma," he tells the kids. "Never forget what she did."

He now serves as Assistant Commissioner of Aviation, in charge of safety and security for Chicago's

Midway Airport. He's on leave, indefinitely, from the Chicago Police Department. "As Assistant Commissioner, I supervise 40 Department of Aviation Security Officers," Jaglowski told PARADE recently. "We secure the perimeter for the airport. We control people who come onto the airport. We also patrol the terminal for criminal activity."

But Greg Jaglowski's new role in life has not erased the memories of his partner. The school where she died was named after her and dedicated to her in January 1990. "I went back there in February to give out an award," Jaglowski said. "They're always happy to see me."

Jaglowski and Ruiz's heroic efforts have been depicted on CBS's "Top Cop" show. Greg Jaglowski narrated the segment but, he says, "It's so hard to talk about it to anybody. The girl that portrayed Irma, it was a good feeling to tell her about different things, how it is working in the squad car and working together almost four years." Jaglowski says his emotional wounds have not really healed. "Whether I go to an award ceremony, or do a TV show, it's still tough talking about it. In the TV show, I wanted to make mention of other people who got killed. But when I talk about my partner..." Jaglowski stops to regain his composure. "Nobody else can understand what you've gone through. The part you relive, whether it's my incident or any other police officer's incident, there's something that keeps coming back. It's like a video camera in your mind."

In addition to the Officer of the Year Award, Jaglowski has been honored by national and local groups. He was chosen to meet President Bush at the ground-breaking ceremony of the National Law

Enforcement Officers Memorial. Standing at the President's side that day, Greg Jaglowski represented all law enforcement officers.

"It made me feel good to be recognized," he says. But there's always a sadness to the accolades he receives.

"It's still just a solemn thing because I'm getting the awards alone, without Irma."

CHAPTER 4

"SECRET WEAPONS" IN SERVICE TO AMERICA'S YOUNG PEOPLE

Contrary to public opinion and the stereotypes promoted by television shows and movies about police work, law enforcement officers generally spend only about 10% of their time making arrests. The other 90%? Helping people—often going out of their way, on their own time, to reach out to the community, especially to youngsters in need of a helping hand.

Many officers are dedicated to this particular kind of "social work." But perhaps none has done more than Captain Richard Z. Voorhees, a small-town cop who initiated a nationwide program that has led to the rescue of thousands of runaway kids.

For his outstanding work with youth, Captain Voorhees, 46, of New Jersey's Bridgewater Township Police Department, received the 19th annual police service award given by PARADE and the International Association of Chiefs of Police in 1984.

Young people have been Captain Voorhees' life. During his years on the Bridgewater police force, he has rescued, counseled, arrested, and befriended hundreds of children. "When it comes to the youth in the community," said the chief of police, Dix Fetzer, "you just might say he's the town's secret weapon."

Once, several years ago, a runaway girl from a troubled home in Bridgewater called Voorhees in the middle of the night to ask for help. She was in Florida, alone and destitute. He quickly wired her money for the bus ride home. But he knew there had to be a better way.

Voorhees came up with his solution in 1984. In a

letter to Trailways Lines Inc. in March, he proposed that the bus company offer runaways a free ride home from anywhere in the country.

"There are so many kids who want to get back home after they've run away," says Voorhees. "They're out on the streets for a while, and when they get tired of it, they don't know which way to turn."

On June 7, in response to Voorhees' letter, Trailways introduced "Operation Home Free," a national program that gives runaways the chance to get home—no questions asked. To qualify, any runaway child simply appeals to a police officer. The cop then verifies the youngster's status and arranges for a free bus ticket home.

In the program's first two months, 543 young people were reunited with their families, said Roger Rydell, a spokesman for Trailways. In its early days, the program averaged ten reunions a day.

There are some personal reasons why Voorhees takes quiet pride in helping young people. He was left at the age of 16 to fend for himself when his mother died. "I just didn't have anyone to turn to when I wanted to," he recalled. "I was alone. That's why I have a good feeling when kids do call me when they're in a jam. Maybe it's the father image—trying to give them some direction."

For years, Voorhees has personally had an "open door" policy for any youngster, no matter what he's done wrong. Late one night more than a decade ago, for example, a teen was being chased on a drug charge by the police in another town. But instead of heading for the state line, he sped directly to Voorhees' house.

Voorhees did end up arresting the youth—but only after a man-to-man talk and some fatherly understanding.

As for his own three kids—Christine, Richard, and Craig—they never doubted for a minute that their dad had the stuff of heroes. When told of his PARADE/IACP award, daughter Chris said proudly, "I knew Dad would make No. 1."

Today, Voorhees is "Chief" Voorhees. The program he started, "Operation Home Free," which gives runaway teens a free bus ticket home, is still going on under the auspices of Greyhound Lines, Inc. Greyhound's Liz Dunn calls Voorhees a "voice for the runaways. He's worked hard to keep the program going."

By 1990, the program Voorhees started had reunited about 25,000 teens with their families, a remarkable achievement of which Chief Voorhees can be proud.

He Builds a Bridge Between Kids and Cops

When Officer Wesley W. Ridlon of the Portland Police Department came to the end of a "rap" session on drug abuse at a school for delinquent boys, one of the wayward teenagers approached him and mumbled, "If I'd had a chance to meet you a year ago, I don't think they'd have had to send me to this place."

Wes Ridlon was touched because nearly all his work as a law enforcement officer is in trying to build a bridge between kids and cops, trying to convince skeptical schoolchildren that the police are "human guys" vitally necessary to the orderly conduct of society. For this important work, Ridlon received the 1971 Police Service Award conferred by PARADE and the International Association of Chiefs of Police.

"Kids are surely the most important resource we have," said Ridlon, "Personally, I shudder at the thought of alienating them and I can't see any reason why police work should be performed in a way that turns them off. We have got to show them that we're important to each other."

Ridlon's usefulness to the school kids of Portland, and by extension to the entire community, was seen in many ways. He recalled that when he first began going to the schools he would hear mutters, "There's a cop. Wonder who he's chasing." But soon they ran up to him with a "Hi, Mr. Ridlon. Are you gonna give us a talk today?" And everywhere he went about the city, he was greeted by his young friends. He visited them at schools and playgrounds for all sorts of group activity—lectures, film and slide demonstrations, bicycle rodeos and just plain rapping. And they came to him, more and more of them, as individuals with problems.

Assistant School Superintendent Clyde Bartlett reflected on Ridlon's approach: "As good a way as any to measure the success of Wes Ridlon's work is in the numbers of youngsters who seek him out after school hours and ask his advice. They'll often go to him rather than their guidance counsellors. That's pretty fine praise for a police officer."

Ridlon recounted: "I never cease to be amazed at the variety of problems bothering kids today: How far can the police go in searching a car for beer cans? If a young fellow drinks moderately at a school dance, can he still get in trouble? If you're at a party and drugs are being used, but you don't know it, why is it the police can still arrest you? Frankly, I can't answer all their questions to their satisfaction. And if I can't, I level with them. You have to do that. A kid can spot evasion immediately.

PARADE watched Ridlon in action before a group of disadvantaged young women and saw an example of his honest approach. One of them said, "You people make a big thing against narcotics but still you'll use alcohol. Aren't you a hypocrite?"

"All right, you've put me on the spot," Ridlon conceded. "I'd have to admit that if it's true the heroin user starts on marijuana, then you can say the alcoholic starts on beer. I won't defend the use of alcohol but I will say that on the average it doesn't have the savage destruction of narcotics or the need to turn to crime to get it."

Ridlon, a member of the Presidential Honor Guard during his U.S. Army days, probably worked harder than a conventional policeman in his devotion to Portland's 17,500 school children. In 1970 he gave nearly 600 talks. His rap sessions in the high schools—called Problems of Democracy—proved so popular that the youngsters have asked that they be converted into a formal course with academic credit. As a result, Ridlon became a "schoolteacher" as well as a policeman, teaching a Community Awareness Program. The kids insisted that they wanted to put questions to "the people who run the community" so Ridlon brought in the city manager, finance director, public health officer, city councilmen and others who could answer the students' searching questions.

He constantly tried to give the youngsters a piece of the action: "At a parochial high school I asked them to tell me how the police department could be administered better. One of the things they came up with—they actually figured out that we could save several thousand dollars a year by buying smaller but more deluxe patrol cars because we'd get more money when we turned them in."

Portland Police Chief Douglas W. Steele praised Ridlon's efforts: "Wes Ridlon's enthusiasm in working with school youngsters is creating a new climate among them as far as police work is concerned. Obviously, we can give the community better service if we have the cooperation of our young people. Wes Ridlon may create a whole generation of law abiding citizens."

Ridlon doesn't pretend to aim that high. He has encountered some of his former "customers" from Portland High School at the delinquent boys' school. They're now inmates.

But other cases gave great satisfaction. Once he "took charge" of a 16-year-old girl whose family had left her at loose ends. Shy and nervous, she'd taken to marijuana and speed pills. After she took an overdose, Ridlon helped place her in a mental health clinic. When she emerged, he had a supermarket job waiting for her. First she worked behind the scenes, then was moved out to face the public as a cashier to overcome her shyness.

Ridlon was delighted that this young woman "made it" out of a tough situation.

Ridlon recalled an incident that amused him. Two boys were riding patrol with him while making a "documentary" on police work with a camera and tape recorder. A pair of young toughs came along and began to yell provocative taunts at Ridlon. The documentary makers had become so identified with Ridlon, the policeman, that they urged angrily, "Let's arrest those guys."

One of the most poignant moments in his career with kids came after he'd noticed that one long-haired, sloppily dressed boy always seemed to sneak furtively into Ridlon's Problems of Democracy class. This went on for weeks. Finally a teacher at the school happened to see the boy. The teacher came straight to Ridlon and told him the boy had been expelled from school a month ago. But he was still coming back to rap with a cop. That indicates the caliber of performance that has made Officer Wes Ridlon the Policeman of the Year in 1971, and Sheriff of Cumberland County, Maine, today. He ran unopposed for the office in November 1990.

Sheriff Ridlon updated PARADE on his continuing work with kids: "I'm in charge of community relations, the 'Officer Friendly Program.' It's a Sears Roebuck Foundation program that brings police officers into the school system. We talk about stranger danger, school bus safety, bicycle safety. Now I do it under the auspices of the Sheriff's office. I've been here for about eight years. I retired from the Portland Police force in 1976 after 20 years in the Portland department. I was a community relations officer."

Ridlon says the introduction of drugs into the schools is the biggest change he has seen in police work over the course of his career. Perhaps that new and terrible danger to youngsters is one reason Wes Ridlon continues to work in law enforcement. But he also says it's in his blood.

The people of Cumberland County, Maine, are glad Wes Ridlon's still on the job, helping kids find a sure footing in troubled and troubling times.

In addition to Richard Voorhees and Wesley Ridlon,

many other PARADE/IACP honorees have been lauded for their outstanding work with young people. Here are just a few of the stellar examples:

Officer Moses Webb, Menlo Park, California, Honorable Mention, 1974.

A community relations officer, Webb found the key to halting juvenile vandalism of houses repossessed by the Federal Housing Administration and Veterans Administration—which had been costing $100,000 a year. He got the VA and FHA to hire ten neighborhood youths at $50 a week as junior housing inspectors. They quickly identified vandals, got them to refrain, talked to parents. Result: vandalism dropped 50 percent and dozens of other cities asked Menlo Park for Webb's formula.

Officer William Hunter Hyatt, Lakeland, Florida, Honorable Mention, 1977.

As a police officer and member of the International Brotherhood of Magicians, Hyatt used both elements at appearances in local schools. After warming up his audiences with magic tricks, Hyatt would give a crime prevention talk, often stressing traffic safety and the tragic consequences of drug abuse.

Officer Dennis J. Fitzgerald, New York City Police Department, Honorable Mention, 1976.

Here's a shooting specialist who works with basketballs rather than bullets. Fitzgerald started by organizing police basketball teams and bringing in neighborhood kids to watch them play. Then he expanded the program by organizing contests among the youngsters —some of which took place at intermission time in Madison Square Garden pro games. Private business donated funds to buy T-shirts and basketballs as prizes, and the project grew to include participation by 150,000 youngsters a year.

Detective Frank Prescott Dawson III, Howard County, Maryland Police Department, Honorable Mention, 1980.

Kids and cops have always had a special relationship—but not always a positive one. Dawson decided to change all that. He created Camp Beartrax, an overnight camp for underprivileged and wayward youngsters staffed by police volunteers.

Trooper Fred Leeds, Illinois State Police, Honorable Mention, 1981.

In his free time, Leeds directed a special institute to prevent teen alcohol and drug abuse. Stressing education and peer leadership, it has involved more than 1,600 youths around Illinois.

Sergeant Robert Gronauer, Las Vegas Metropolitan Police Department, Honorable Mention, 1989.

Fear had hold of Gerson Park, a 300-apartment, low-income housing project with the city's worst narcotics and gang problems, until Gronauer set up a highly visible police storefront. The cops befriended the neighbors, set up a Boy Scout troop and started a job-referral system for teens. Six months later, children were playing in the project's courtyards once again.

CHAPTER 5

"SUPERNARC" AND OTHER MODERN-DAY HEROES

We Americans like to make progress. We're proud of our creative, innovative spirit. And usually, given a decade or two, we can solve a problem—or at least make major inroads in the right direction.

Tragically, this has not been the case where illegal drug use is concerned. Despite the very best efforts of America's law enforcement officers, the sale and use of drugs continue to wreak havoc in our society. Cops face the gravest danger of all as they confront well-armed drug lords and drug-crazed addicts.

Here are the stories of extraordinary law enforcement officers who have been recognized for their roles in the war on drugs by the PARADE/IACP awards.

From Enforcing Laws to Making Them

At 44, Paul E. Fabian was a gentle, reflective man who was happiest when fishing with his son or gardening with his wife and three daughters. It was hard to believe that nearly every day he was locked in battle with that ugly scourge of our times—dangerous narcotics.

As police sergeant in the east central New York town of Rotterdam, Fabian was dedicated to fighting the drug traffic. And he devised a distinctive approach—an immunity deal with young users—so effective the pushers were afraid to enter Rotterdam.

For his outstanding success against a menace that haunts every parent's mind, Sergeant Fabian was named to receive the fifth annual Police Service Award conferred by PARADE and the International Association of

Chiefs of Police in 1970.

There are two notable things to say about Fabian's approach. First, in 1970 he was believed to be the only cop in the country using the immunity weapon against narcotics. Second, the approach was not legal—and he readily admitted it!

"What I do," said Fabian in a 1970 interview, "is go right into the home of a drug-using kid and sit down with the youngster and his parents. I tell the boy or girl that we believe he's on drugs and we want to talk it over. Now, ordinarily, the kid would clam right up and the parents would refuse to believe anything bad about their son or daughter.

"But by special arrangement with the District Attorney's office, I make a deal with the kid. I tell him he has immunity from punishment for anything he's done in the past. I tell him the slate is wiped clean up to the moment. Actually, a policeman has no authority to give anybody immunity, but District Attorney Howard A. Levine has agreed to go along with my approach.

"Almost invariably, once the youngster knows he won't be punished, he opens up and talks a flood. His suppressed guilt feelings pour out. In a healthy way his problem is surfaced right there in the home. And the communication with his parents that got lost somewhere along the line is suddenly renewed."

Police Chief Joseph S. Dominelli of Rotterdam noted the results of nine of Fabian's home interviews. "Five of the teenagers admitted in front of their parents to using drugs, putting the matter right out in the open. Five supplied a total of 41 names of users and pushers, some beyond our town limits. Eight admitted being in groups while drugs were used. Four admitted having underlying problems and two agreed to psychiatric treatment.''

And District Attorney Levine was extremely happy about his ''arrangement'' with Fabian ''because we get such a vast amount of information that we otherwise wouldn't get at all or could get only through many months of investigation. Fabian's experiment is certainly paying off and should be widely imitated.''

As direct by-product, Fabian developed a remarkable number of undercover teenagers slipping him information. And it's this that kept the pushers out of Rotterdam. They never knew whether Fabian would be on the spot waiting for them. Of course, he couldn't stop Rotterdam kids from going off to nearby Albany or Schenectady to meet pushers but, in general, he held Rotterdam's drug problem at bay while in several neighboring communities, the menace was acute.

As a result of his narcotics work, Fabian has some definite opinions on some controversial matters:

• The principal reasons that kids gave in 1970 for taking up drugs were boredom, disrespect for adult leaders, problems with parents, and bewilderment over Vietnam.

• There's no point in arresting teenage users. Get them off drugs or under treatment and make the big effort against the suppliers. ''Put them in jail and throw away the key.''

• Marijuana is not harmless—too often it's the beginning of the road to heroin.

• Congress must authorize at least 7,000 additional Federal narcotics agents if the U.S. is to make any progress against drug smugglers and suppliers.

PARADE accompanied Fabian on a repeat call to a

15-year-old girl and her parents. The girl, who suffers from a deep but unidentified emotional problem, had made six LSD trips when Fabian first began to visit and she'd had some bad experiences. At one point she said she didn't want to live any longer.

The parents, solid, middle-class citizens living in a nice home in a nice neighborhood, admitted frankly that they had no idea the girl was on drugs until Fabian dropped in one evening.

"I was scared to death when he came in," the girl reveals. "Any kid who uses drugs knows about Sergeant Fabian and his surprise visits and some quit on account of that, just to be free of the worry. But when he told me he and the District Attorney would forget all about the past, I thought it was such a break for me and suddenly I wanted to talk about it." The girl saw a psychiatrist and kicked her drug habit.

Fabian was born in Rotterdam and remembers a bucolic boyhood when you walked through forestland to get to the movie theater.

"For years and years you never heard of a drug problem here," he says. "It was a big-city problem only. Then you began to see it moving up the Hudson River from New York, town by town. I began to worry. I asked around, 'What are we doing about narcotics?' The answer was, 'Not much, if anything.'"

As a cop, Fabian began to involve himself in drug problems. He went to Washington and took the two-week course given by the Federal Bureau of Narcotics and Dangerous Drugs. He put together a half-hour lecture and slide program to alarm the town about drugs. He put this show on, often every night in the week, before church and civic groups and in schools. And, finally, he came up with his immunity scheme which District Attorney Levine called "the most original idea in the drug field in a long time. A real advantage."

"In this town I've got 4,000 teenagers to look after," Fabian said. "I need every advantage I can get."

Today Paul Fabian, who retired from the police force as a lieutenant in 1982, is a Schenectady County legislator. He reflects on the success of his program for teens. "My program was on drugs. But the drugs were only a symptom. I'd tell everybody, 'Forget the drugs, correct the system.' Other towns picked up on the idea. We kept up the program for a couple of years. Ninety-eight percent of the kids I dealt with straightened out. A small percentage gave us a problem after we surfaced the problem within the home and let the families handle it. Life is very simple; we make it complicated. If parents were aware that their kids were on drugs, they would handle it. But they don't realize they're on drugs until it's too late."

Rotterdam now has an anti-drug initiative called the DARE program, copied from California. "But it's basically the same thing that I was doing," Fabian told PARADE in 1970. "Policemen go into the schools and confide in the kids. The only difference is that I'd confide my knowledge in front of the parents. As a result, the problem became a home problem, and parents and children could solve the problem together. We would leave it there.

"It's a lot of work to make this approach succeed. We finally ended up hiring a social worker in the police department. I'd talk to a child and his parents, and then the social worker would go in and help. The social worker is still working."

Paul Fabian notes that times have changed since his 1970 award. "Twenty years ago the biggest problem was marijuana. Today it's crack and other drugs." Fabian hopes to continue his anti-drug work in the New York State Legislature.

Call Him "Supernarc"

A decade after Paul Fabian was named Officer of the Year, another anti-drug crusader won the same honor. This former television repairman came to be known as "Supernarc"—and it's easy to understand why.

A lot of folks in the seamy Austin, Texas, underworld of heroin and "speed" would readily admit they were afraid of undercover cop James Wolsch. One thing that set the 32-year-old Senior Patrolman Wolsch apart was that "he's so successful at what he does," said Austin Police Chief Frank Dyson. In a city which Dyson described as "a major stockpile center" for drugs in the Southwest, Wolsch alone accounted for 50 percent of all the narcotics cases in the department, and 25 percent of the cases handled by the other seven narcotics officers.

He got his nickname, "Stoopdown," as a uniformed officer 10 years ago, when he worked the tough 11th Street section of East Austin. Wolsch would hide his car and crouch behind the window of an abandoned motel to watch the dealings of the dope pushers and prostitutes in the area.

"There wasn't a whole lot going on in his district that he didn't know about," said Lt. Bobby F. Simpson, who a few years later picked Wolsch to do undercover narcotics work as part of a newly formed Organized Crime Control Unit.

Wolsch is effective, said his commanding officer, Capt. Gilbert Miller, "because he can blend into any situation. He can go from the high to the low." One day he would be talking chemistry in a clandestine lab where methamphetamine, or "speed," is being produced; the next he would be slapping backs with junkies in the ghetto. Though he wore no wigs or makeup, he could change his appearance simply by changing his hairstyle, which he did three or four times a year. A measure of his talent, said Miller, was that, at the time of the PARADE/IACP award, he had been undercover six years—more than any other cop in the department—despite the fact that the drug traffic in Austin "moves in closed circles."

Much of his undercover work involved making "controlled buys" of drugs from dealers, in an effort to become familiar in the underworld and sniff out the big "fish" who ran large-scale drug operations. Wolsch prepared for his role like an actor getting ready to step on stage. If he was buying cocaine, he'd snort antihistamine and twist the nozzle in his nose to make it red like a "coke freak." If it was heroin, he'd burn his arm with an acid stick to simulate needle tracks.

Wolsch has a reputation for honesty. "It's axiomatic in law enforcement that narcotics officers lie," said Travis County D.A. Ronald Earle. "But I've never known James to lie."

That reputation not only made Wolsch a valuable witness in court. It also made him credible to the informants who put their futures on the line with him in return for information. A good narcotics officer "doesn't ever promise an informant anything he can't legally deliver," said Lt. Simpson. "Wolsch has all this —he can communicate."

What's more, says Simpson, the underworld knew he couldn't be bought. Typical was Wolsch's reaction to the $1 million bribe he was offered to lay off a clandestine "speed" lab. "It was an insult," he said.

Wolsch even earned the respect of some of his criminal adversaries. "He doesn't despise the people he works with the way many cops do," said Capt. Miller. In fact, Wolsch even helped rehabilitate some of the junkies he's arrested.

Danger is the name of the game in undercover narcotics work, perhaps more than in any other aspect of police work, said Capt. Miller, because of the high financial stakes and the use of weapons. But Wolsch seemed blind to its terrors. "There are a lot of people in town who would like to buy James off—or have him killed," said Miller. Once someone almost succeeded. A ring of "pill pushers" hired an assassin to murder Wolsch during a drug buy. He was saved by an informant's call.

Wolsch, whose 1980 salary was $20,000 a year, claimed he was a mediocre high school student who became interested in police work at the age of 20 by riding in a squad car with a neighborhood cop. At the time, he was working as a TV repairman. "If there was a problem I couldn't solve, I'd stay on the job until 10 or 11 until I got it fixed," he recalled.

He approached narcotics work with the same dogged persistence. But on the way to becoming an undercover cop, he made a sacrifice. "We don't do much as a family," admits his wife, Peggy, who was his high school sweetheart.

Wolsch insisted that the sacrifice was worth it, not because of any overriding sense of public duty, but simply because "somebody has to do it."

Today, 11 years after being named Officer of the Year, James Wolsch is a sergeant in the narcotics interdiction unit of the Austin Police Department working at the Robert Miller Airport.

"I've been in narcotics for ten years," he told PARADE recently. "Now I handle a drug dog at the airport. I'm working as an investigator. After the PARADE award, I worked undercover four more years, then got into the canine squad. I like the range of things— everything from interdicting drugs coming into the airport to seizing large quantities of money. There are a lot of people coming here to buy drugs."

Wolsch says he misses undercover work. "But I'm getting older and was ready to get out of it. Austin's a big town, and you get where too many people know you and the risks get too high."

Wolsch hails changes in police work over the last decade that have made things a little easier. "It's a whole lot easier for us to do background checks. It's the computer age. The canine squad has developed over the last five years. Everybody uses it now. Customs has used it all along."

Labrador retrievers named Jack and Pete accompany Wolsch in his work today. They sniff out marijuana, cocaine, heroin, and methamphetamine, and they check cargo, luggage, and all the checked luggage and freight.

"Supernarc"—a.k.a. "Stoopdown"—celebrated 20

years in the Austin Police Department October 1, 1990.

More Heroes in the War on Drugs

Drugs and drug-related crime pose the largest challenges to law enforcement in the United States today, according to many authorities. Since 1966, the PARADE/IACP awards program has recognized scores of officers who have made significant contributions in this ongoing battle, among them:

Lieutenant George C. Austin, Jr., Newport News, Virginia, Honorable Mention, 1967.

One of the first Blacks to achieve high police rank in Virginia, Austin has been assistant to chief of detectives for several years. A graduate of the Federal Bureau of Narcotics School in Washington, D.C., and instructor in that field in several police in-service schools, he was credited with breaking up several narcotics and numbers rings.

Captain Lynn Rudolph, Kokomo, Indiana, Honorable Mention, 1973.

Captain Rudolph is a prime example of a specialist many law-enforcement agencies find indispensable— the narcotics expert. Widely in demand as a speaker all over his state, Rudolph increased drug arrests fivefold in four years as head of a special investigation unit. Sometimes he went underground to develop informants, and frequently posed as an ex-addict who kicked the habit.

Detective Louis Isnardi, Nassau County New York Police Department, Honorable Mention, 1978.

Answering a routine request from Michigan police to check a phone number, Isnardi ran into dead ends that aroused his suspicion. The result was an investigation involving Scotland Yard and Dutch police. It ultimately led to the arrest of 36 persons and the seizure of 50 pounds of heroin worth millions.

Special Agent Theodore Wood, Drug Enforcement Administration, U.S. Department of Justice, Honorable Mention, 1981.

Working undercover in a dangerous two-year drug-smuggling probe, Wood and his team obtained indictments of 194 people and seized billions of dollars worth of contraband, including a million pounds of marijuana, $1 million in cash, and 26 boats.

Special Agent C. R. Gordon, U.S. Drug Enforcement Agency, Honorable Mention, 1982.

Bleeding from a bullet in the neck, Gordon, a drug enforcement agent, fired a shot to warn his colleagues moving up a dark staircase toward a gunman. He then persuaded the suspect to surrender.

Detective Michael McClary, Las Vegas Metropolitan Police Department, Honorable Mention, 1984.

His undercover probe of heroin smuggling in Las Vegas took him into the criminal underworld of Bangkok, Thailand, where he repeatedly placed his life on the line to help ensnare two major Thai drug kingpins. Their arrest stunted the heroin trade in cities as widespread as Las Vegas, Paris, and Melbourne.

Special Agent William Wolfe, Florida Department of Law Enforcement, Tampa, Honorable Mention, 1984.

He directed the investigation of what is believed to be the largest ring yet charged with cocaine smuggling. The smugglers were accused of bringing into the U.S. nearly 16,000 pounds of cocaine estimated to be worth $2.2 billion. Forty-two persons were indicted.

Special Agent Roy Garcia, Illinois State Police, Honorable Mention, 1987.

Piecing together a puzzle of arrests and dope seizures, he uncovered a large-scale drug conspiracy stretching from the Midwest to Mexico. After a three-year investigation, the ring finally was cracked, largely as a result of his actions.

Special Agent Houston E. McNeal, Virginia State Police, Honorable Mention, 1987.

Undercover for two years with the FBI, McNeal posed as a drug distributor in order to nab 16 corrupt officials who were smuggling cocaine into Eastern Kentucky. A key witness, McNeal must keep his appearance and whereabouts under wraps.

Officer Wayne Barton, Boca Raton, Florida Police Department, Honorable Mention, 1988.

Barton drastically reduced drug sales, then initiated a neighborhood cleanup campaign and started summer and after-school programs for youths. It's no wonder that Barton is called "the Pied Piper of Boca Raton."

Detective Frank A. Perez, Dallas Police Department, Honorable Mention, 1988.

Working undercover, Perez helped bring in 186 suspects on major drug charges. He is responsible for the seizure of more than $3 million in drugs. He asked that his photo not be used.

Police Officer David Magnusson, Miami Police Department, Honorable Mention, 1989.

On Patrol in Miami, Magnusson has become a one-man war on drugs. He parks his squad car and walks, watching for crimes in progress. Frequently he finds them. Last year, he made 230 felony and 68 misdemeanor arrests. In four years on the police force, he has received 30 commendations.

Sergeant C. David McCoy, Dallas Police Department, Honorable Mention, 1989.

McCoy heads a squad of detectives whose cocaine and currency seizures accounted for about a third of the division's haul over the year. He was also the hero of a daring gun battle during a "buy-bust" operation that pitted him against two suspects who had just killed one of his squad members.

Sergeant Gene Farmer, Fort Lauderdale Police Department, Honorable Mention, 1989.

Farmer devised an anti-drug program that hits crack dens with vigorous building-code enforcement. In less than two years, his team—which, along with Farmer, includes a fire marshal, building inspector and city prosecutor—has demolished 84 crack havens and secured 258 others, prosecuted 200 landlords, and inspired nearly $30 million in private investment in the community.

Major Archie Hatcher, Tampa, Florida Police Department, Honorable Mention, 1990.

Tampa's crime rate plunged 12.4 percent last year—a drop officials credit, in part, to QUAD (Quick Uniform Attack on Drugs), a program directed by Hatcher. Begun in 1989, it has increased police-citizen cooperation and stepped up drug arrests. In each of the city's four "Quads," teams of specially trained cops monitor areas of peak drug traffic. Result: Of 141 active "dope holes," authorities say, 84 percent now show little or no street drug sales.

Captain Joseph R. Farmer, Phoenix Police Department, Honorable Mention, 1990.

Farmer used powerful promotion techniques to drive home an anti-drug message to recreational drug users. Under the slogan "Do Drugs. Do Time," Phoenix and 25 other police agencies in Maricopa County, Arizona, have banded together. Everyone who gets caught using drugs, even a small amount, is thrown in jail overnight and then given the option of a treatment program if he has no previous criminal record. Farmer, a former narcotics commander, retired in July 1990.

And, last but never least, PARADE/IACP and the entire law enforcement community join in saluting a man who made the ultimate sacrifice in the fight against drugs—

Special Agent Enrique Camarena
of U.S. Drug Enforcement Administration,
honored by a posthumous citation in 1985—the first
in the history of these awards.

Camarena's exceptional work against Mexican
organized-crime figures will never be forgotten. His
effort led to the seizure of money, assets, and drugs
valued in the hundreds of millions of dollars. He was
abducted, tortured, and killed in Mexico in the line of
duty, February 7, 1985.

CHAPTER 6

"GREAT COPS": WOMEN WINNERS OF THE PARADE/IACP AWARDS

Greg MacAleese, 1977 Police Officer of the Year, thinks it's high time a woman officer received the same honor. "One of the major changes in police work has been the influx of women," he said recently. "It's improved it. They bring a level of intensity and dedication to the job. A lot of talent, a lot of brains. We had a lot of female detectives in violent crimes. They're very good interrogators. They also have an ability to get in and defuse some situations."

PARADE/IACP awards have gone to many women officers, starting with Policewoman Madeline Baker of Columbus, Ohio, in 1968. This veteran homicide detective's distinguished career working on murder and assault cases called on her to risk danger often, sometimes as a decoy. She was the first woman detective in Columbus.

As the role of women in law enforcement grew over the years, their names began to crop up more frequently on the PARADE/IACP annual awards listings.

Finally, in 1990, a woman officer received the highest honor bestowed by PARADE and the International Association of Chiefs of Police.

Katherine P. Heller, who risked her life to save a fellow officer, embodies the courage, commitment, and compassion that have marked a quarter century of Police Officer of the Year.

"I didn't have time to taste the fear," said Officer Heller in an interview with PARADE. Heller's decisiveness should lay to rest any doubts about women's abilities as police officers, asserted U.S. Park Police Chief Lynn Herring. "I hope her example will encourage young women to make the leap to law enforcement," he said.

It all started on a drizzly evening about 7:30 p.m. on February 22, 1990 in Lafayette Park, across from the White House, where Kathy Heller was on foot patrol. Officer Scott Dahl had dropped by on his motorcycle to give her a package. As he was leaving, he saw a man with a gashed head staggering in the park. "That guy just hit me with a brick," the man muttered, pointing at a vagrant across the street.

While Dahl crossed the street to investigate, Heller checked the wounded man, who was bleeding profusely. But looking up in Dahl's direction, she saw two figures grappling on the ground.

The vagrant had attacked the officer and begun digging at Dahl's eyeballs. As the officer shouted for help, Heller rushed to his aid and beat the attacker over the head repeatedly with her nightstick. Finally the man seemed to back away—but he had grabbed Dahl's gun.

The two cops ran for cover. With the attacker stalking Dahl around a car, Heller moved in close behind a metal electrical box on the sidewalk. As the man leveled his gun at Dahl, Heller stepped into the open to position herself for a clear shot.

Then, as Officer Dahl dived for cover, Heller fired. The bullet struck the man in the pelvis, but he didn't flinch. She pulled the trigger again. This time, her target slumped to the ground, fatally wounded in the heart. The 24-year-old vagrant, Russell Baits—who, police say, had a history of convictions and violent behavior—later died at the hospital.

"I wouldn't be here today if it weren't for Kathy," said Officer Dahl, an ex-Marine who has been on the Park Police force for three years. "She saved my life."

Heller's heroism came as no surprise to those who have worked with her. From the time she joined the Park Police in March 1988, she has earned a reputation as an aggressive cop who has a knack for digging behind a case to find trouble. "She always seems to be where things are happening," said Capt. Benjamin Holmes, Jr., her former commanding officer. In 1989, she ranked sixth out of 350 patrol officers on the force in making felony criminal cases.

"My biggest asset is my mind," said Heller, who is 5 feet 3 inches tall and weighs 107 pounds. "Ninety percent of my adversaries will be bigger than I am. Hopefully, I can out-think them."

What's more, said Capt. Hugh C. Irwin, her former lieutenant, Kathy Heller also has what many other female cops possess—an ability to defuse tense situations. "You can talk somebody into handcuffs," she said. "When you acknowledge your limitations, you can beat almost anything."

What drove her to the police in the first place? The eldest of five sisters, Heller, who's single, found high adventure within the walls of her Potomac, Maryland, bedroom reading Jack London, Louis L'Amour, and Alistair MacLean.

"I had lessons in piano and voice, but I wanted to break free," said Heller, whose mother wouldn't let her play sports for fear she'd get hurt. "I was a wild spirit. I wanted to be out there like Sea Wolf, pirating ships."

After college, where she earned bachelor's degrees in

science and geology, she worked at jobs ranging from seismologist to interpretive ranger. Through a ranger friend, she learned about the Park Police, a branch of the Department of the Interior that was started in 1791 to protect federal lands and buildings in Washington, D.C. Today, the Park Police encompasses a force of 650, including 62 women, who police the capital region along with federal parkland in New York City and San Francisco.

Heller loves police work so much that when she was offered limited duty after the shooting, she turned it down. Group therapy sessions with other police officers involved in shootings helped her put the incident behind her. She returned to work after two and one-half months and asked to be assigned to the city's tough Anacostia beat, which she patrols in a cruiser.

"As a police officer, you live on the edge," she said. "I went over the edge and was able to come back. But I can never be the same."

Officer Heller's colleagues know that she will go on to distinguish herself throughout her career. Along with a grateful America, they hail her achievements and those of the thousands of other women serving with distinction in law enforcement agencies across America.

Detective Susan Johnston, Kansas City, Missouri, Honorable Mention, 1972.

A specialist in self-defense, Detective Johnson was a principal factor in raising the arrest-for-rape rate in Kansas City from 57 percent to 74 percent. She trained more than 3,000 women in how to avoid danger in personal attack. "I fight dirty," she said cheerfully.

Sergeant Lorraine Owsley, Anne Arundel County, Maryland, Honorable Mention, 1973.

Sergeant Owsley had performed in many fields of police work, but she specialized in child abuse cases, sex offenses against minors, domestic problems, and prevention of delinquency. Because of her tact and ability to gain the trust of minors and women, she was frequently called in when off duty to help out in emergencies. She also lectured often on the subject of self-defense for women.

Detective Eileen Lindstrom, Superior, Wisconsin, Honorable Mention, 1974.

Detective Lindstrom, a specialist in crime prevention, had been a police officer for 24 years at the time of the award. In a city of 33,000, most of her work dealt with women and girls, but she also found that troubled young boys were receptive to a woman officer. Her philosophy: If young offenders are dealt with in a kindly manner, they won't return as police problems when they're adults.

Detective Mary A. Glatzle, New York City, Honorable Mention, 1975.

A member of the city's street crime unit, Glatzle had made more than 250 felony arrests at the time of the award, many by acting as a decoy. She would sit seemingly nodding on a bench in Central Park, purse open beside her. What was not visible was the .38-caliber revolver in her belt. Her record for one night was five arrests. Colleagues called her "Muggable Mary."

Sergeant Patsy G. Noble, Sacramento, California Police Department, Honorable Mention, 1976.

A specialist in working for the youth of her community, she served countless hours of her own time counseling boys and girls who are on paths that can lead to trouble. Sports and music are among the fields in which she tried to enlist the interest of the young. Yet she was known as a tough cop, too. At the start of her career, Sergeant Noble passed for three months as an addict in the seamy world of drug selling and came up with evidence that sent five men to jail.

Agent Sara Niell, Mississippi State Bureau of Narcotics, Honorable Mention, 1977.

Sara Niell, 25, was involved in a drug bust with a male colleague. At a rendezvous, her partner was wounded by fire from nearby woods. She stood in the open and shot it out with the attacker. Afterward, Niell took the colleague to the hospital. While she was there, a drug dealer she had wounded showed up for treatment—Niell arrested him immediately.

Officer Giovanna Punneo, San Jose, California, Honorable Mention, 1978.

San Jose State University was terrorized by a number of sexual assaults, and Punneo volunteered to be a decoy. As she wandered through the campus one night, a 240-pound man came up from behind, put a knife to her throat and said, "Come with me or you're dead." She whirled and shot him in the chest. Supporting officers then took over.

Officer Lucille A. Franckowiak, San Antonio, Texas Police Department, Honorable Mention, 1979.

Just 25 when she received this high honor, Officer Franckowiak put her life on the line many times during undercover work in narcotics and vice investigations. Franckowiak's work through 1978 resulted in felony cases against 175 defendants while on narcotics duty. Some were indicted as habitual criminals and received life sentences.

Detective Virginia Guzman, Brighton, Colorado Police Department, Honorable Mention, 1980.

A former welfare recipient, Guzman set a personal example off duty and on, which has had a dramatic impact on the community. In her work as a Community Services Officer, she developed creative outreach programs, including summer rap groups for teens and family-oriented treatment and prevention programs for runaways.

Officer Nancy LaBadia, Medina City, Ohio Police Department, Honorable Mention, 1981.

As the city's first crime-prevention officer, she began a program that in just one year was named Ohio's best, featuring a network of CB radio crime-stoppers and a neighborhood crime watch.

Officer Wendie K. Harper, Tacoma, Washington Police Department, Honorable Mention, 1982.

Officer Harper showed exceptional courage in capturing an armed robber who had wounded two victims. Stalking the suspect in a dark alley, she returned his fire and wounded him, instead of taking cover and calling for help.

Officer Connie Higgins, Louisville, Kentucky Police Department, Honorable Mention, 1985.

Responding to a routine call at an apartment, Higgins met disaster. A man pulled a gun at close range and shot her three times—once in the face. "I knew I couldn't take another hit," she said. Higgins returned the fire, killing her assailant. Her valiant effort not only saved her own life but also the lives of a young couple who, unknown to her, had been held hostage.

Police Officer Norma Jean Amaral, Seekonk, Massachusetts Police Department, Honorable Mention, 1988.

Bystanders had backed away from the cab of a burning pickup truck, but Amaral smashed the windshield with her foot and a fire extinguisher and pulled the trapped driver to safety.

Officer Susan A. LaGray, Charlotte, North Carolina Police Department, Honorable Mention, 1988.

Awakened by screams, LaGray saw a man stabbing a woman. The man escaped by car, but not before LaGray called in his license number and radioed for help for the victim. The suspect was arrested, and the victim is alive today.

CHAPTER 7

"ALL IN THE DAY'S WORK":
DONALD E. RASK,
DENVER POLICE DEPARTMENT

The two nights began very much the same for Patrolman Donald E. Rask of the Denver Police Department. But the endings were quite different. For on one of those nights, duty called upon him to save five people in a blazing building. On the other, duty compelled him to kill a man in a dark cellarway. And in each case the young policeman risked his own life—just part of a job for which he was paid $646 a month.

These sample exploits in Rask's career—the rescue of five people amid choking smoke and the shooting of an armed sniper—illustrate vividly the extremes of emergency that routinely confront the uniformed patrolmen who make up the backbone of any police force.

In his early years on the job, Rask faced loaded guns and flashing knives. He hauled in burglars and helped solve murders. He cracked a car theft gang and kept his cool in tense racial situations. And he was extolled for such a simple virtue as gentleness in helping an ill citizen.

"This officer does an excellent job," says a line in Rask's personnel file which is laden with commendations from his superiors. For his sustained "excellent job" as a patrolman, Rask received the third annual Police Service Award conferred by PARADE and the International Association of Chiefs of Police in 1968.

Although Rask loves police work and can't imagine any other career, he got into it late. Interviewed at the time he received the Police Service Award, Rask explained that Denver is his home town and after high school he spent two years in the Army and eight in civilian jobs before joining the force in 1964.

"I'm not sure just why I did it," he mused. "I remember I started at $475 a month, a cut of more than $100 from the job I had. But I was tired of desk work and today I think the job I have is the best one in the world. You never know what's around the next corner. There aren't many jobs around that give you that kind of excitement."

Rask spent more than three years on routine patrol, but in 1968 he was a member of the Special Services Unit which his chief, George L. Seaton, described as "a highly trained detail of hand-picked personnel." On this assignment, Rask left his wife and daughter each evening, about the time the sun sets behind towering Mt. Evans off to the west, and joined a patrol partner. In their patrol car, the two drove back and forth all night through high crime areas and, as Rask observed, "Anything might happen and I prefer night work because the situations tend to be more interesting."

In one seamy neighborhood, there stood an old red brick house in which something did happen to Rask. It's succinctly stated in his file: "This officer, in answering a disturbance call, was compelled to take a human life."

"I can still see it—that rifle pointed right at my belt buckle," Rask recalled slowly. "We had answered this call. Somebody in the house was shooting out from windows. It was about midnight. We went down this narrow cellar stairway. There was an opening off to the left and my partner eased over there. I was still on the stairway keeping my flashlight on the door at the bottom.

"Just then the door opened a crack and the rifle barrel poked out pointing at me. Remember, six shots had already been fired in the last few minutes. I began yelling out, 'This is a police officer,' over and over. The rifle stayed on me and I had no place to go. Then it was pushed out further. Seemed like I was gonna get the next bullet. I started shooting. I got off four shots and my partner over at the side got off three. We found the man with the rifle dead behind the door. Turned out he was an alcoholic who had hallucinations that he was being attacked.

"I didn't feel good about it. Nobody wants to kill a person. But if anybody questions my shooting, I'd just ask him to put himself in my spot. As a formality, my partner and I were both charged with murder and both acquitted."

Rask says he doesn't worry at all. Like most policemen, he knows there's danger in his job but he reasons that once he's prepared himself as best he can to face it, there's nothing more he can do. He discusses quite routinely his staring at that rifle barrel, or groping through the smoke-filled apartment with visibility zero, his tortured lungs burning and an unconscious man in his arms. "All in the day's work," says Rask.

But there's something for which he has strong emotion, monumental anger. That's the ambushing of policemen in which officers are lured to a scene on false alarms and then gunned down, some murdered, some gravely wounded.

"If someone wants to shoot a cop," says Rask, "he's got all the advantage. It's easy to set us up because it's our duty to respond to calls. We have to go. I can really burn when I think about police ambush."

Rask likes his work so much he calls it his main hobby and he invites others to share it. When the Denver police decided to make a TV recruiting ad, Rask was chosen to speak the message. He's not sure how effective it was but he knows he made an impact in his own home. He remembers hearing little Dione complain to her mother: "I was watching Bugs Bunny and they stopped showing him and started showing Daddy."

Today Donald Rask is still with the Denver Police Department as a Sergeant. "I spent most of my career on the street," he told PARADE in 1990. "Now I'm in charge of the fugitive and bomb unit. Catching criminals is my specialty. We go after felons from all over the U.S. The fugitives include murderers, rapists, bad check writers—America's most wanted. The fugitive unit gets calls from all over the U.S. Denver is a place where they seem to gravitate."

After 27 years with the Denver Police Department, Rask still derives great satisfaction from his work. "These people that we're apprehending are not assets to society. They're doing crimes every day of the week to survive. Very seldom do they get a legitimate job. When you remove some of these people from society, you're assured they're going to be put away for a long time. That's real rewarding."

But, like most veteran police officers, Sergeant Rask has known the "down" sides of law enforcement work, too. "I've been involved in four different incidents where lives were taken; I've been sued for $26 million, but never lost a case; I've been in a couple of shootouts; I've apprehended a rapist who ended up dying on me. He was good for seven rapes. I've never been wounded, but I received some injuries. My knees have been operated on. I've had six surgeries as a result of police work—twice on my knee. In my last arrest, for example, I went over a wall after a kid and landed on my knee. Had surgery in '81 and in '83.''

These hard knocks don't diminish Rask's enthusiasm. He says he'll consider retirement—someday. ''When I get around 30 years in the department I'll consider it. I'm too young to retire!''

CHAPTER 8

A DIFFERENT KIND OF OLYMPIC VICTORY

He pulled off a "mission impossible"—making the 1984 Olympic Games safe from terrorists. His chief hailed it as "the accomplishment of the century in law enforcement." And that is why Cmdr. William M. Rathburn received the 20th annual police service award given by PARADE and the International Association of Chiefs of Police in 1985.

Rathburn spent five years planning in minute detail a vast security network necessary to ward off a terrorist attack. "It had to be a plan that was foolproof, with no weak spots," said his superior, Los Angeles Police Chief Daryl Gates.

From the outset, said Rathburn, "I felt a strong responsibility to protect the image and the reputation of the United States. There were a lot of people—particularly those from other countries, who did not believe that a democratic society could protect itself."

The real test seemed to arrive on the opening day of the Games, when all of Rathburn's careful plans threatened to go up in flames with the Olympic torch. Moments before President Reagan was due to arrive at the Los Angeles Memorial Coliseum, an engineer inspecting the giant torch noticed some suspicious wires leading to a box near the top. He was convinced it was a bomb set to explode when the flame was lighted.

Within minutes, an airborne bomb squad helicoptered to the site to disarm the mechanism. The box turned out to be nothing more than an ABC microphone—installed to enable the television audience to hear the "whoosh" of the torch as it burst into flames.

"I was still holding my breath," admitted Rathburn in a 1985 PARADE interview, "when Rafer Johnson actually started lighting the torch."

Soon after, terror descended from the skies. A small, fixed-wing aircraft started flying straight for the Coliseum, where the President was arriving to welcome 90,000 spectators and an estimated 2.5 billion TV viewers worldwide.

Two police helicopters, positioned in the sky, were ready for action. In a scene right out of Rambo, the helicopters moved together to provide an airborne blockade for the plane—and the plane turned tail as the helicopters gave chase.

The police finally caught up with the interloper on the ground. By that time, the passengers had run off, and the pilot, who had a long criminal record, was arrested.

Rathburn admitted that, despite all precautions, there were limits to what the police could do in such circumstances. Had the plane continued to move in on the Coliseum, he said, "We were not going to shoot it down—that was clear. The damage we would do from a plane crash might well be greater than any damage they'd do on their own."

At stake during the 16-day period were the lives of 5.8 million spectators and 11,000 athletes, coaches and trainers from 140 countries. During the Games, they were spread over about 150 miles of Southern California at 22 Olympic sites.

To police such an operation, some law-enforcement officials were even talking about suspending civil rights guaranteed by the U.S. Constitution, according to Rathburn. Others—like retired Army Col. Charles

Beckwith, who commanded the aborted hostage rescue mission in Iran—thought the job couldn't be done without a "security czar" who could rule with an iron hand.

But Rathburn rejected such suggestions. With his low-key leadership style, he brought together more than 50 independent law-enforcement agencies—including the FBI, the Secret Service, the Los Angeles Sheriff's Department, and the California Highway Patrol—and forged them into one smoothly flowing cooperative team. They were ready to respond at a moment's notice to any crisis.

More than 100 threats came in during the Games. Among them was a particularly ominous tip from overseas: The Israeli team would be attacked by Palestinians en route from the airport to the Olympic Village at UCLA.

Rathburn's team swung into action. They blanketed the airport with security people and then provided the Israeli team with a heavily armed Presidential-style motorcade to UCLA. No attack ever materialized.

"I think terrorists and other people who wanted to disrupt the Games were just outnumbered," said Harold Ezell, a federal official who was on Rathburn's planning team. "We had more resources in place than most countries have in their armed forces!"

Rathburn also was relentless in anticipating trouble, Ezell said. Take, for example, the strategy he came up with to protect that same Israeli team from a repeat of the terrorist attack that left 11 athletes dead at the Olympic Games in Munich in 1972. Before the Soviets pulled out of the 1984 Games, Rathburn suggested that their team should be assigned rooms that would, in effect, "wrap" them around the Israeli team. That way, he figured, any terrorists would have to penetrate the Russians first.

"The Israelis loved it—and the Russians wanted nothing to do with it," said Rathburn with a laugh.

When that proposal went sour, Rathburn did the next best thing. He housed the Israeli team behind two layers of security fences rigged with alarms. In addition, he placed cement barricades disguised as decorative plant-holders at vital points around the perimeter. The barriers were intended to prevent a suicide-style car bombing similar to the one that destroyed the U.S. Embassy in Beirut.

At the time of the PARADE/IACP award, Rathburn was commanding officer of the Support Services Bureau of the Los Angeles Police Department and, as such, was responsible for its communications network, computer operations, scientific labs, and city jails.

PARADE's 1985 Policeman of the Year was matter-of-fact about his Olympic-victory. "You just try to do all the right things," said Rathburn. "And then, with enough luck, you're successful."

Since the PARADE/IACP award, Rathburn was named Deputy Chief of LAPD in June 1986. In a 1990 interview he told PARADE, "For the last two and a half years, I've been in charge of the South Bureau, South Central Los Angeles, in the harbor area. We handle all of the basic police services. It's a very difficult area: 58 square miles, 24,000 identified gang members. It's got the highest concentration of gang members in the city. We average one murder a day. I've spent a lot of my career working South Central LA. I was a policeman here in '65 during the riots; in '69 I was a sergeant, an adjutant to the deputy chief. I liked the area, know the area well. There are 550,000 people in this area.''

Rathburn says some of the anti-terrorist skills he developed in running Olympic security help him today. ''We're coordinating with agencies at all levels of government. We're a lot more successful because of the assistance of other agencies, such as the FBI, probation and parole.''

In March 1991, William Rathburn's talent, hard work, and leadership abilities landed him a prized assignment: Chief of Police, Dallas, Texas. This ''Olympic hero'' now leads a major police department. Undoubtedly, he'll continue to display the qualities that led to a terrorism-free 1984 Summer Olympic Games, and the 1985 Police Officer of the Year Award.

CHAPTER 9

LIGHTS, CAMERA, AND *POLICE* ACTION

Most law enforcement officers enter the profession hoping to avoid media exposure. After all, the average officer appears in a media spotlight only when he or she has faced grave danger or sustained wounds. But two of the PARADE/IACP Police Officers of the Year actively sought prominent roles in their local media—not to achieve personal stardom but to enhance their police work through effective use of the radio and television airwaves.

"Hello, This Is 'Buzz the Fuzz,' and You're on the Air!"

Most police officers detest the term "fuzz," so often thrown at them with hostility and disrespect, especially by young people. But in Dayton, Ohio, Police Sgt. James R. Hopkins encouraged citizens to use the word when they phoned in their problems and questions to him on his weekly radio program, "Buzz the Fuzz." Between 1975 and 1982, for 90 minutes every Tuesday evening, "Fuzz" Hopkins sat at a microphone at a local station and answered a great variety of these telephoned queries—some of them, he says, almost frightening. Samples: I'm 14 years old, how do I get a gun? Could I really get six months in jail for driving without a license? Can I legally kill a man who's stealing my property? What happens to a cop who takes a bribe?

Hopkins—sometimes crusty, sometimes humorous, but always informative—patiently replied to the questions, and if he didn't have an answer immediately, he promised to supply it on the next program. Frequently he even invited people to come to his office at headquarters for further discussion. And they came.

Because of his enlightening radio program and for superior performance in his regular job—supervising a nationally known pioneer project that invited Dayton citizens to help plan police policy—Sergeant Hopkins received the 11th annual Police Service Award conferred by PARADE and the International Association of Chiefs of Police in 1976.

Sergeant Hopkins began his police life 25 years before receiving the award, as a cop on the beat. There he learned almost immediately the philosophy that dominated his thinking and his activities as a policeman: "There is no way that you can effectively police a city unless there is a cooperation and understanding between the police and the body of citizens. And the better that understanding and cooperation, the safer the city, the better a place to live in. In my radio show—that title "Buzz the Fuzz" is funny—I tried on my own time to help build a bridge between police and civilians. If I succeeded, everybody was a winner.

Interviewed at the time of the award, Sgt. Hopkins explained, "In my regular daily capacity as a police officer, I'm the coordinator of our Policy-Making Bureau, which I'm told may be the first of its kind in the country. Policy-Making Bureau might sound like an innocuous phrase, but to some cops it's dynamite. It means setting up a series of task forces each composed of, say, four policemen and four civilians. They sit down together in meetings over a period of weeks and try to set up guidelines on how policemen should act in various situations: use of force, high-speed chase, kid's curfew, shoplifting, domestic squabbles—probably a dozen categories.

"You can see the possibility of controversy. Some old-line police officers grumble and say, 'No civilian is gonna tell me how to do my job.' I understand why they feel that way. Many an older cop grew up professionally on the theory that the police are somehow supreme. But that's not true. Police are service people for the public which pays our salaries. It's logical and proper that we get their views on how they want to be served."

Dayton Police Chief Grover W. O'Connor agreed: "We're very happy with our civilian contacts, and Sergeant Hopkins is great on developing them because he's a guy who can always see both sides of any disagreement. He's consistent and trusted by other policemen who might be a little leery of civilian advice. I'm 36 years on the force and up from the bottom, and for the first time we're getting a real written framework on police action policy in various situations. When I was a young officer, we worked under the rule that the chief is always right. But now we've come to realize that no longer makes sense.

"A prime example of a good result from one of Hopkins' police-civilian task forces is in the field of hot pursuit. We've all read about those 90-mile-an-hour chases that so often end up in crashes and injuries or death not only to cops and suspects but to other people caught up in the impact. Well, we formerly didn't have exact rules on hot pursuit. The officer in the squad car usually acted on impulse, was driven by a bulldog syndrome, and believed that the chief expected him to 'get that man.'

"Now, as a result of one of Hopkins' task forces, we

have specific guidelines. The pursuing officer knows that he might take into account other factors than just 'get that man.' Icy streets, fog, heavy traffic, children's playground ahead, chance of accident, suspect's car capable of faster speed than police car—items such as these have to be weighed against the importance of the chase. If risks seem too great, the chasing officer knows he is authorized to give it up."

Sergeant Hopkins, as coordinator of policy-making, sat in on most of the meetings involving police and citizens. He remembers how some of the participants came up with opposite and sometimes surprising arguments:

"In discussion on the use of force, there was this civilian who said bluntly, 'You can't do police work without force. You've got to sock 'em in the head when they get out of line. None of this pussyfooting about their rights.'

"And in the same group was a 28-year-old police sergeant who's had his share of rough experiences trying to enforce the law. He said: 'I've had to use force plenty of times, but I know that I can't bust heads just for the hell of it and then hide behind my badge. Not in Dayton. I put a curb on my use of force according to that written body of rules that we and the civilians agreed on.'

"In the force category several policies emerged regarding use of guns by police. One was that, in general, you never shoot a man in the back. If he's going away, let him go. Another was that you don't press that trigger unless the suspect makes a first move."

Here are some of the Policy guidelines created by

Dayton's Policy-Making Bureau under the leadership of Sgt. Hopkins:

• Shoplifting—formerly the police took the word of the store and booked the suspect. Now they must investigate. Is the accused out of work? Are there needy children at home? Is he or she a mental case needing help? Sometimes they tell a store that no case has been proven and if complaints are to be made, let the store first sharpen its own security measures.

• Domestic squabbles—formerly the cops had two choices: make an arrest now or threaten to make one if a return visit is required. Now the police have a list of 18 special services available around the clock seven days a week in such fields as alcoholism, child care, and mental health.

• Curfew—the law says that under age 14 a kid must be indoors by 10:30 p.m., save for a few emergency exceptions. But the new guidelines apply some common sense to this. The police recognize, for example, that there's a great deal of difference between being on the loose aimlessly in a gang after 10:30 and playing quietly in front of the family home with neighbor boys and girls.

• Off-duty guns—formerly a cop could carry any sort of handgun, even an exotic one with far-out ripping firepower. Now he can pack only the standard police .38.

So sensitive is the relationship between police and the public that Dayton's policy-writing program has attracted wide attention. By inquiry or personal visit, police departments have looked into it from California, New York, Tennessee, Minnesota, Wisconsin, Texas, and Calgary in Canada. "It's a compliment to be noticed that way," said Hopkins, "and we welcome all comers. Whatever we've learned, we'll share with anybody."

Civilian task force members also appreciated their partnership with police. Said George Pearce, a retired design engineer: "It was great to sit elbow to elbow with those bluecoats and know they wanted your help. I'd like to do it again, but I think more people should be drawn in." And Lilla Dumas: "I never dreamed the police would ever ask me for advice. I always thought of them as some vague force with strong power out there in the city, but I got to know them as nice people who have all sorts of problems and want help in solving them."

"That's exactly the spirit and cooperation that we need from the citizens," says Sergeant Hopkins, Policeman of the Year. "In many cities they review police incidents after they've occurred. We try to anticipate and make up the rules ahead of time. So, let the people keep on buzzing the fuzz one way or another and we'll all understand each other better."

Sgt. Hopkins retired in 1982 and went to work for the Southland Corporation as Assistant Manager of the bad-check unit. In 1986 he retired and does "as little as possible!"

In a recent interview, James Hopkins reflected on the heightened dangers police officers face today. "I got out of it just ahead of crack. We had heroin, marijuana, cocaine. Now it's almost a full-time operation. Crack has almost taken over the police department's activities. I wouldn't want to be there today. It's a dangerous job today more than it was when I was there. Crack dealers have automatic weapons. We never faced that in my era."

Top Cop Makes Money Talk

In 1976, an Albuquerque cop named Greg MacAleese created a project that's still achieving solid results. The Bible says money can be "the root of all evil," but in the MacAleese anti-crime program it's the root of much good. Through a fund raised by hundreds of residents, the city pays cash to informants for clues leading to arrests and indictments of malefactors. In its first 11 months of operation, total payments were more than $11,000 in amounts ranging from $50 to $2,000. Some results: 261 cases including murder, rape, robbery, and burglary solved in less than one year, plus recovery of $286,000 worth of stolen property and a citywide crime reduction of 27.6 percent.

And widespread praise. Albuquerque Police Chief Bob V. Stover pronounced the project—called Crime Stoppers—"an unbelievable success." Chief Deputy District Attorney Robert A. Martin said in a letter to City Hall: "Of all the devices and programs that have come along in the area of law enforcement in the past few years, this is one that appears to be a sure winner. I sincerely hope that it can be continued and expanded."

For his imaginative anti-crime project—a precursor of today's nationally televised shows like "America's Most Wanted"—Greg MacAleese received the 12th annual Police Service Award conferred by PARADE and the International Association of Chiefs of Police.

The designation of Greg MacAleese as the 1977 Policeman of the Year points up that more than ever police are groping harder for ways to reverse the trend of increasing crime. MacAleese, a former college baseball pitcher who had offers from five major league teams, calls the Crime Stoppers program "simply an exchange of commodities." In a 1977 interview, MacAleese explained, "Out there in the community are people who have information about crimes. We want it. And in exchange we'll pay the money and guarantee anonymity. Sometimes we get the criticism that paying informers is a sort of smelly business. But I don't see it that way. It's commonplace after some sensational or especially repulsive crime for a reward to be offered for information. We just have a permanent setup of reward. I think about 70 percent of our telephone informants are ordinary people who happen to hear or see something, and the rest are in or of the underworld."

A keystone of Crime Stoppers is publicity to keep the Albuquerque community fully aware of how it can help the cops by telephoning a special number at police headquarters. MacAleese used three TV stations, eight radio stations, and two newspapers. Even car bumper stickers urged cooperation.

Crime Stoppers' most novel gimmick was "The Crime of the Week," a three-minute show written by MacAleese depicting an actual crime in Albuquerque. The young officer rounded up amateur actors, coached them through his script, and they appeared every Monday night on a TV news program. A typical reenactment involved a case of rape, and within a minute of its conclusion there was an anonymous phone call offering to help.

"There's psychology behind these shows," MacAleese said. People are more likely to react to visual treatment. It tends to jolt their memories, to sharpen a sense of awareness of something they know about somebody.

One man said to me, 'You seem to be saying I should turn in my neighbor.' I told him, 'Well if he's a crook, I hope you do.' But we do get calls from people who wouldn't call the police directly. We are set up as a civilian and community organization, and that gives us a special status.

"We had a gas station robbery on 'The Crime of the Week' that brought 30 phone calls. Four of them proved to be meaningful, and our detectives arrested the guy within 48 hours. We paid out $1,000 on that one. There was another case of murder by ambush. A woman phoned in the tip and eventually decided to testify in court. The killer was convicted and got 15 to 55 years in prison. Of course, if a person agrees to testify, the anonymity can't be guaranteed. But in cases in which the anonymity holds, courts here have ruled against defense lawyers who demand to know the identity of accusers, and even the American Civil Liberties Union hasn't challenged those rulings.

"In one particularly brutal murder, after the conviction a witness received so many threats against himself and his family that we sent all four of them hundreds of miles away, got him a job and gave the whole family new identities. It was not only a humane thing to do, but it showed the underworld that Crime Stoppers stands by its informants."

Albuquerque Police Detective Joe Garcia said, "What we've done is to create worry and suspicion among part of our criminal element. If they had a code of honor about squealing on each other, we've cracked into it. A hoodlum worries to himself, 'So and so might sell me out for $500.' Planting that attitude among the street crime perpetrators does a lot of good for the community."

Crime Stoppers also pioneered the TV display of mug shots of suspects. Said MacAleese: "We put a mug shot on the screen on Monday night and almost invariably we've got the guy by Wednesday. Somebody out there knows where he's holed up, and in come those phone calls."

Detective Sara Billingsley of the sex crime division added this case history: "We had a string of five rapes in cars in the parking lot at a shopping center. This man was extremely vicious. In addition to the assault, he'd click a gun at a woman's head and get a thrill from her terror. Crime Stoppers put a mug shot of a suspect on TV and an acquaintance phoned in almost immediately. We arrested him and he was sent away for a long, long time."

Crime Stoppers' fund that pays informants now stands at more than $37,000. Back in the beginning an appeal was sent out along with the water bills, and that brought in about $10,000 in amounts from $1 to $10. But, as the program becomes better and better known, contributions arrive almost daily. The smallest was 36 cents from a fifth-grader who explained in a letter, "It's all I can afford."

The largest was $5,000 from the One Hundred Club, an organization of community leaders who rush to the financial aid of the families of policemen and firemen killed in the line of duty. Jack Mulcahay, club president, told PARADE: "We were concerned about the increasing crime rate in Albuquerque. We felt that if money can be a weapon against it, let's use it. We had a special interest because, since we were formed in 1971, we have paid out assistance money on three occasions. Each time it was to the family of a policeman killed in action. For us it's been great satisfaction to watch the Crime Stoppers' performance.''

MacAleese personally made the payoffs to the informants and, because he received telephoned threats to his own life, he dictated the site of the meeting for his own safety and made sure that he was paying the right person. He made payoffs in such places as men's rest rooms, deserted gasoline stations, parks full of people, and lonely mountain roads.

The 1977 Policeman of the Year began his career as a street cop. He experienced violence—one time a gun and another time a knife was pulled on him—but his only injuries resulted from a beating by eight kids in a parking lot. Later, during a year as collector of evidence for detectives, he found that many shady characters had impulses to divulge information if they could do so safely. That was one of the elements that led to Crime Stoppers.

Albuquerque Police Chief Stover called MacAleese "the sparkplug that makes Crime Stoppers work."

The young officer said he enjoyed his achievements but that occasionally he wondered how he might have fared as a major league baseball pitcher. Still, he said, it's rewarding to be striking out criminals.

Interviewed recently by PARADE, Greg MacAleese reports that he's still in "show business" as President of Mast Communications, a television production company in Dallas. He has helped to implement the Crime Stoppers' concept elsewhere with tremendous success.

"In 1984, I took leave of absence from Albuquerque to run the Texas Crime Stoppers Advisory Council. I got that up and running, and after three years I was ready to come back. The Greater Dallas Crime Commission heard I might be available, and I was with Crime Commission for the next three years.

"In January of 1990, I created a TV show called 'Texas Crackdown,' about the effect of drugs in the Dallas-Fort Worth area. It was a two-hour show, which outlined a three-pronged approach to the drug problem. First, we had a 'Crime Stoppers Tip Line,' manned by narcotics detectives, to take tips from citizens on local drug dealers. We used street footage, profiled six of the most wanted. We received 977 tips in four hours. Secondly, we tried to encourage those who were addicted to get help. For them, we had a help-line put together by reps of various counseling groups, manned by doctors. We had 1,030 calls to the 'help line.' Finally, we tried to educate the public on the impact of drugs.

"The show was a tremendous success. It earned the highest ratings for any one show in local TV history. As a result of that show, other communities started to call us. Demand was so great, I had to leave the Crime Commission."

MacAleese started to create similar shows for other cities. "We estimate we'll do 20 shows around the country in the next year. They are locally produced. They emphasize effects of drugs at the local level." MacAleese is pleased that his original spots on Albuquerque TV news laid the groundwork for "America's Most Wanted," "Unsolved Mysteries," and similar shows. "As a result of the publicity from the Police Office of the Year Award, we had police departments all over the world contact us about Crime Stoppers," MacAleese explained. "Now we have almost 900 branches of Crime Stoppers around the world. It's an independent, non-profit corporation with a civilian board of directors. We wrote a manual, put together a national organization called Crime Stoppers International. We helped communities get these things started."

Greg MacAleese started a program with an unbeatable track record. "Calls to Crime Stoppers have solved more than 300,000 felony crimes. In the last 15 years, $1,000,400,000 in stolen property has been recovered. Crime Stoppers is now in 13 different countries. And it continues."

The work of James Hopkins and Greg MacAleese shows the importance of creativity in police work. MacAleese sees it this way: "In order to improve policing, we have to continue to search for creative ways to counteract crime. The criminals aren't sitting still. They're looking for new ways. If we're not creative, we're going to continue to be left behind."

And every law enforcement professional knows we can't afford to let that happen!

CHAPTER 10

EXTRAORDINARY, ORDINARY HEROES

Many of the law enforcement officers honored by PARADE and the International Association of Chiefs of Police since 1966 took part in a special drama: a Presidential assassination attempt, the Olympic Games, or a single, seemingly superhuman heroic deed. These rare occasions showed the officers at their best, and focussed a national spotlight on their skill and valor.

But the PARADE/IACP awards have also singled out another kind of hero. These men compiled extraordinary records of service and heroism in years of police work they thought of as "routine"—though to most people, stopping burglaries, preventing rapes and murders, and "busting" drug kingpins hardly qualifies for the term!

Let's meet these extraordinary, ordinary policemen, starting with the first recipient of the PARADE/IACP Award.

They Called Him "Mr. Homicide"

Sgt. Philip T. Dwyer of St. Louis was probably the only pistol-packin' P.T.A. president in the nation in 1966.

The veteran officer, on the job a relentless homicide detective, off it a gentle man who worked with children, was a 57-year-old father of six, grandfather of four, and nemesis of hundreds of criminals when he accepted the award. Learning of it, he reacted briefly in terms of personal satisfaction, but then remarked, "You know, the force can be proud."

And proud indeed was St. Louis Police Chief Curtis

Brostron—for his force, for himself, and for Sgt. Dwyer. Holding the little blue card that summed up Dwyer's 33 years in the department, Chief Brostron observed:

"Ten departmental awards have gone to Phil Dwyer, including the Meritorious Service Award—the highest one we have. If you had a couple of thousand Phil Dwyers, you'd have quite a force."

"Of course there are some bad cops and I wouldn't defend them for a minute," Dwyer said in an interview in PARADE in 1966. "But the police don't always get a full understanding from the public. For example, take that cry of police brutality. There's no way in the world for a policeman to handle a resisting person than by using the necessary force. And that's no justification for hollering 'police brutality.' Speaking personally, I like my job and I'm proud of my record and I simply want to ask those who scream loudest against the police, 'Would you like to try living in a city that had no police?'"

A few of the cases Dwyer worked on:

A patrolman gunned down in a holdup. . .an elderly woman strangled in her home. . .two women shot in a bar. . .a woman strangled in the back seat of her car. . .a college student stabbed after a basketball game. . .a woman raped and murdered in a rooming house. These have been typical Dwyer problems.

If a "typical policeman" is a somewhat grim fellow, cold-eyed, a bit beefy and all business, Dwyer did not qualify. There was a mild quality to his appearance; he could easily be cast as a teacher. This observation caused August Ernest, chief of detectives, to explain:

"I don't mean to imply that Phil Dwyer pushes

people around but he long ago demonstrated that he can take care of himself when necessary. This is not a pantywaist.''

At St. Elizabeth's Academy where Dwyer served as P.T.A. president at the time of the award, he again was not what he seemed. The principal, Sister Angeline, said:

"He's so refined, so dependable, so courteous, I have to pinch myself to realize that he carries a gun and deals with murderers. To us he's a persuasive man who knows how to get people to serve on committees.''

That same persuasiveness has pulled a confession out of many a killer, but that aspect matters little to the kids at Mark Twain School's playground. As Dwyer strolled into the playground one day, a chorus of ballplaying moppets cheered:

"Here comes the Sergeant! Here comes the Sergeant! It's his turn to pitch!''

Dwyer's even temperament enabled him to move without shock between these two worlds—from singing ballads around the living room piano to investigating a slum hellhole where a homicide victim sprawls.

"Nature has fortified me against the blues,'' he said. "This is my job and I do it.''

Dwyer said that assembling sufficient evidence for convictions was getting harder all the time because of court crackdowns on use of confessions. But he welcomed the challenge:

"I'll tell you one of the greatest kicks in police work. It comes when you know you've got the right guy, the one who pulled the trigger—but he won't confess. And then you go out and dig up enough evidence to make him end up saying 'All right, I did it.'

"And you get your evidence by hard work, door-to-door drudgery, asking questions. You ought to see me laugh at the TV crime shows. All that stunting. In a way they're the funniest shows on the air."

Not funny to Dwyer was the refusal of people to cooperate with police, the reluctance to become involved. He didn't mind if they played hard-to-get for awhile—in fact, he enjoyed a bit of cat-and-mouse trying to coax a witness or suspect into talking. But flat refusal burned him up.

"I had this case of a woman and two men in the front seat of a car. In the back were her five kids, the oldest about 12. One of the men pulled a gun and killed the other. The woman wouldn't answer a single question and she told her kids not to answer. A great way to teach children respect for the law."

Like many cops, Dwyer puzzled long and hard over man's reasons for murder. "Not long ago," he recalled, "we had a fellow killed in a tavern for singing in the wrong key. Can you imagine that? Another one was stabbed to death because he borrowed a nickel and played a jukebox tune the lender didn't like."

Dwyer's lineage is Irish as far back as he can trace. He was born in St. Louis' Kerry Patch section and as a youth was called "Fire Engine" because of his red hair. Today, it's dark brown; he doesn't know why it changed. His father died early and Dwyer spent several years in an orphanage before joining his mother and stepfather. The need to work made him a high school dropout but he attended night school and got his diploma. He was a 50-cent-an-hour spot welder in 1933 when a neighbor told him of an attendant's job in a police garage. Its $110 a month smacked of security to the 23-year-old, and he took it. In 1966, Dwyer was putting his life on the line for the people of St. Louis for $736.66 a month.

Only three times in his career had Dwyer pulled his own trigger. He had never killed anyone, although seven years ago he plugged a wrench-wielding assailant in the legs, and the man later jumped to his death from a hospital window.

Would it bother him to kill a person? "Yes, I think it would, even if I'd have to do it to protect my own life. I've had plenty of chances to shoot at people running away from arrest but I just couldn't do it."

Dwyer and a crew of colleagues received a big compliment in 1966 after their crisp, efficient investigation solved the savage murder of Joseph Klearman in his coal yard. In a few days a large billboard across the street from Police Headquarters blossomed with this message: "THANK GOD for our POLICE DEPARTMENT."

It was signed, "The Family and Friends of JOSEPH KLEARMAN."

In a letter to the department, Melvin Klearman, the victim's son, saluted the police who "day in and day out . . .confront men of violence, risking their lives."

Dwyer minimized the danger in his job but admitted that he never told his wife, Imogene, ahead of time if he had a perilous assignment.

"No use her worrying," he said.

But she did. At the top of the stairs in the Dwyer home stood an Infant Jesus which she illuminated the moment her husband left for work. "This means Somebody's watching over him," she said.

The Dwyers are a very close family. The father has

seen so much sordidness and how easy it is for young people to slide into serious trouble, that at times he was overstrict with his children. Said Imogene, one of the four Dwyer girls, "Daddy would look our dates over so closely, the poor guys thought they were in a police lineup. Once he sent a boy packing because he didn't take off his hat."

In a final peek at Sgt. Philip Dwyer in 1966, he was at his fourth-floor desk in Police Headquarters, a desk jammed with such crime mementoes as pistols, loaded dice, checkbook from an abortion case, and all sorts of pictures of malefactors. The first winner of the Public Service award had two things nagging at his mind— when he could find time to go to Texas and run down a lead on a recent, gruesome St. Louis murder, and who he might get to take over the entertainment committee at St. Elizabeth's P.T.A.

PARADE caught up with Philip Dwyer in 1990. The 80-year-old Dwyer reported, "I retired in '74 as a sergeant. Then I worked for the Sheriff's Office for seven years. I was with the St. Louis Police Department for 42 years. I'm still in contact with the homicide section."

Dwyer said it was easy to stay motivated in his career in law enforcement. "I liked homicide work. I put 21 years in that. When you get involved in that walk of life, you can always find something to do. There's always an open case to check up on; always plenty of work. It kept me busy. The time just went by." He cites as his greatest achievement during his police career solving a lot of homicide cases. "I was pretty lucky with that assignment. I worked with some nice men. No homicide is worked out by itself. My partners were hard workers. It was very rewarding." Dwyer saw a huge increase in homicide cases over his 21 years in that field. "When I started out, we had 75 cases. By 1974, we had 270 cases in one year."

Dwyer's advice for young cops, including grandson Edwin Menzenwerth, a policeman in St. Louis: "Stick to the truth all the time. You should never exaggerate on a case and try and make it, because if you do, they'll catch up with you on the witness stand. Stick to the facts."

His Dog Was His Partner Against Crime

"I'm not trying to put down the human race," says Patrolman Jake Miller, of the New Orleans police force. "It's just that I believe that a dog is a far more useful patrol partner for a cop than any man could ever be."

Jake Miller was speaking in praise of his own patrol partner, Rebel, an 85-pound German shepherd which "arrested" a record number of criminals. Every working night the team of man Miller and dog Rebel prowled the backways of New Orleans in a police car, and so effective were they in catching malefactors, saving lives, and generally serving the public that they became a New Orleans police legend and accumulated all sorts of awards.

In 1972, Patrolman Miller received another—the seventh annual Police Service Award conferred by PARADE and the International Association of Chiefs of Police. He was the first such honoree to have a canine partner, eight-year-old Rebel. The New Orleans police dog, so gentle that children pet him and romp with him, could also be so ferocious that gun-wielding criminals were reduced to whimpering surrender. Ninety-eight percent of the time, Jake Miller used him only as a threat.

"I don't want to hurt anyone," said Miller in a 1972 PARADE interview. "In seven years on the force I've never once drawn my gun on the job. And Rebel doesn't want to hurt anyone, either. He much prefers to wag his tail. And when a burglar or some other lawbreaker sees the two of us together—I weigh 235 pounds and once had a tryout with the Denver Broncos—they usually sort of think it a good idea to give up.

"The way it most often goes, I come across a building I figure has been broken into. I yell into the darkness, 'Police! Come out with your hands up!' If I get no reaction I yell again, 'I've got a police dog here and I'll send him in if necessary.' That usually does it. Once they come, Rebel seems to regard police work as some sort of game. He practically grins at the people he 'arrests.'

"He's had his lumps, though. One guy managed to throw him down a stairwell in a school but he came right back and cornered the burglar. Another burglar tried to stab both Rebel and me with a sharp screwdriver. Another thing about my partner—he demonstrated the other night that he's 'only human.' We were patrolling out of the car on foot in a secluded area when Rebel took off with a great commotion. My adrenalin cooked up and I wondered how bad this one was going to be. Can you guess what he was chasing—a rabbit. But I regard Rebel as a loyal and reliable friend. He's very devoted."

So was Patrolman Jake Miller. Commented Clarence B. Giarrusso, New Orleans Superintendent of Police: "Dedicated is the word for Miller. I'd like to have a whole force of Millers. He's quietly efficient and people like him. He does his work almost unobtrusively, but when you need him badly, he's a ball of fire.''

Said Miller, ''Well, if I do my work well, it's because I love my work. I can't imagine doing anything else. I can't think of any job that lets you do good in so many different ways. There's just no end to the situations that come up to face a cop unexpectedly.''

Miller, an exceedingly shy man despite his mighty muscles, encountered one of these situations not long before receiving the PARADE/IACP award. He was exercising Rebel in a park by the Mississippi River when two girls dashed up and cried out that two little boys were in trouble out on the river. They had been on a Huckleberry Finn-type homemade raft which suddenly broke apart. One kid seemed to be making it toward shore but the other, clinging to a piece of wood, was swirling out into the center of the river in strong current.

''There wasn't any time to spare on that one,'' recalled Miller. ''While I was running toward the scene, I shucked off my jacket and gun belt. I should have taken off my shoes and this heavy police shirt, too, but there just wasn't any time to reason that out. Well, to cut the details, I got to the boy, broke his stranglehold on my neck and brought him ashore.''

Miller shivered over leaving on shoes and shirt. ''That could have cost my life and the kid's.''

The New Orleans Police Department was more explicit. In an official publication, it observed: ''There is no doubt that without the heroic action of Patrolman Miller, this young boy would have drowned.''

Miller received one of his many departmental commendations for that exploit, and he's also been honored by such groups as the American Legion, Holy Name Society, and City Council.

Rebel and Miller are widely appreciated. Said Acting Sergeant Edwin Hosh, the K9 commander: "Rebel is the best dog we've ever had. He's made the most number of captures. And Jake Miller, who prides himself on being a career cop, is the perfect example of dedication to his job. He puts in so much work on his own time. In police work, you know, it's fairly easy just to go through the motions. Not this fellow. He's for real and every new young officer on the force should use him as an example."

NYPD's Most Decorated Cop

Sgt. Robert A. DiMartini, the most decorated policeman in the history of "New York's Finest," got into his profession almost by accident. A cousin who was scheduled to take a written police test asked DiMartini to come along just for kicks. He did so, took the exam on impulse, scored ninth among 4,800 and thus began a lifetime career abundant with awards.

For his outstanding performance as a lawman in New York City's crime-ridden borough of the Bronx, Bob DiMartini received the 13th annual Police Service Award conferred by PARADE and the International Association of Chiefs of Police (IACP).

At the time of the award in 1978, Bob DiMartini had racked up 191 departmental recognitions for superior police work, and 24 more were pending. He had been shot at and beaten up. He had stared down the mouth of a jittery loaded shotgun, risked his neck in high-speed chases, and offered himself in disguise as decoy for savage muggers. "I enjoy police work," he told PARADE.

His commanding officer, Capt. James Trainor, commented: "There are lots of good cops, but DiMartini is one of the few great ones. He has a very active sixth sense. He can smell crime. And he's aggressive and goes after it."

DiMartini patrolled at night in civilian clothes in an unmarked car. One of his greatest assets as a cop was that while he was tough, alert, and aggressive, he was also gifted with poise and common sense. Once he chased an armed robber to the third floor of a South Bronx tenement. With gun drawn, he rounded a corner to find the robber waiting, also with gun in hand.

"I could have shot him, and then he would have shot me," DiMartini recalled, "and that wouldn't make any sense. We were only five feet apart, so it was certain that somebody would get hurt. I decided to try to reason with him. I told him that as things stood, all he had was a robbery conviction and a few years in the pen. If he killed me, it's murder first degree. Or maybe I'd kill him. I said, 'Isn't it best if you just drop your gun and come along with me?' Fortunately, he agreed."

For performance both intelligent and courageous in just over nine years of police work, DiMartini had won the following departmental citations: one Combat Cross, an Honorable Mention, two Exceptional Merit, six Commendations, 57 Meritorious Police Duty, and 124 Excellent Police Duty.

PARADE asked DiMartini the reasons for his great success as a cop: "One of the most basic items in law enforcement is to have a sharp awareness. You see a window open, a gate ajar, some kids hanging around a store area at 3 a.m. Also, I work hard at my job. I think of it as a profession and I'm proud of it. Another thing—I work in a high-crime area where there are plenty of chances to make arrests.

"And I've been lucky to have great partners. There's nothing more important in police work. When two cops work together night after night, they have to think alike and act alike. In lots of situations there's no time for conversation or questions. If I see something suspicious and suddenly draw my gun, my partner, Frank Adams, does the same."

DiMartini constantly used the phrase "bad guys," but not with rancor. "I was born and raised in the Bronx," said the sergeant, "and I've known minorities and underprivileged all my life. I know the forces of poverty and a broken home and peer pressure that can drive a kid into crime before he knows what has hit him. I don't hate the bad guys. Life is just a contest—it's us against them. If I felt I had to hate them all, I'd end up with ulcers. No way to live."

But contemplating some of his young bad guys depressed him. "A lot of them just have no values of any kind. They don't believe in anything. What can you say about a kid who'll kill an old woman with a knife to get her welfare money? Who'll club an old man to death for $58 in loot just because he's an easy target?"

When DiMartini and colleagues arrested a 19-year-old for subway station robbery, the prisoner began "singing like a bird" about a ring of young crooks who specialized in terrorizing old people in the apartments. This led to the establishment in the Bronx of the Senior

Citizens Robbery Unit—a prototype in the nation—which set up concentrated protection for a highly vulnerable segment of the population.

If you measure police performance by statistics, Sgt. DiMartini emerges supreme. The special, handpicked night squad that he commands averaged 70.5 arrests per policeman over a seven-month period. In the same interval, the average for the bulk of the Bronx force was 2.4 arrests per policeman. That's one reason why DiMartini's commander, Capt. Trainor, observes: "Obviously the sergeant and his men are doing something right."

Robert DiMartini retired from the NYPD in March 1989, after 20 years. "I retired as a lieutenant," he told PARADE in 1990. "When I retired, I was in charge of the city-wide anti-crime unit, a plainclothes crime unit that worked the entire city, predominantly in the midtown area." He retired as the most decorated policeman in the history of the department, with 483 different awards from the Police Department.

Though Bob DiMartini misses his law enforcement colleagues, he doesn't miss the job. "Where you used to be able to be a cop and do your job, today you can't. I saw more people who tried to do the right job get in trouble. The atmosphere has degenerated. I feel for these kids who come on the job today. We live in a society that has no qualms about killing cops, because of the money involved in drugs. These guys are making thousands of dollars a day, and if you get in their way, they're going to kill you. When I was starting out, I don't think it was as bad as it is today. Then at least you knew who your enemy was."

DiMartini counts himself among the lucky police veterans. "I had very good partners, and we're all still here, thank God. Out of all the squads I ever had, none of my troops ever got hurt—thank God. If a little bit of what I did rubbed off and kept them alive, I'm thankful about it."

The National Law Enforcement Officers Memorial Fund and its supporters are thankful, too—thankful for the daily bravery of officers like Philip Dwyer, Jake Miller, Robert DiMartini, and thousands of their colleagues.

CHAPTER 11

"MY DAD'S A HERO":

FBI Special Agent Edmundo Mireles, Jr.

"I'm interested in the other award winners," says Richard Beckman, PARADE/IACP winner for 1988 and a hero in his own right. "I saw a made-for-TV movie about Ed Mireles (FBI) called 'The Miami Shootout.' I'm in awe of what that man had the ability to do. He held it together. Everybody's getting killed, everybody's down, and he knew what he had to do. A man who's wounded who takes the initiative to attack his attackers. I'm in awe."

Sergeant Beckman is one of millions of Americans who salute the uncommon valor of FBI Special Agent Edmundo Mireles, Jr., who survived one of the bloodiest battles in FBI history. Mireles, a 6-foot, 250-pound special agent with the FBI, had fainted a month earlier when a nurse drew blood for his annual physical. Yet he found in himself the courage and stamina to keep shooting—though badly wounded and bleeding—as he led six other special agents in a deadly gun battle with two bank robbery suspects in Miami last April. Two FBI agents and the two suspects died, and five agents were wounded.

For his action, Mireles, a 33-year-old former Marine from Beeville, Texas, received the 21st annual PARADE/International Association of Chiefs of Police service award—a well-deserved recognition of his extra-ordinary courage.

The day of the shootout began with Mireles and his partner, Special Agent John Hanlon, joining a stakeout of several banks in South Miami. They were looking for two men and a stolen Chevrolet that had been used in a bank robbery the week before. Abruptly, the car— occupied by two men later identified as William Matix and Michael Platt, two Army buddies who had become partners in a lawn-care business—was spotted by another special agent. Mireles and Hanlon chased the suspects and tried to bump them off the road.

Mireles and Hanlon's vehicle veered off the road and struck a wall, but another agent, Dick Manauzzi, rammed the suspects' car into some nearby trees. Platt and Matix jumped out and began blazing away with a shotgun and a semi-automatic rifle.

Other FBI men quickly joined the fight. Mireles was shot in the left arm as he ran to take cover behind a car with Special Agent Gordon McNeill. "It felt like some-one hit me with a sledgehammer," recalls Mireles. "I looked at my arm. It was completely shattered. I thought, 'They're going to have to amputate.'" Blood was also running from a wound in his head.

"All hell was breaking loose," he adds. "I could hear shots to my right and shots to my left. I tried to push up with my left arm. Nothing happened. As I tried to push up again, I saw Gordon get shot." Hit in the hand, the agent fell behind Mireles. Later, McNeill was hit a second time.

There was a lull in the fighting, and Mireles couldn't see the suspects. He crawled around the car for a better look. Special Agents Ben Grogan and Jerry Dove were dead, and John Hanlon lay immobilized by his wounds.

Platt and Matix had jumped in one of the FBI cars and were about to escape. But as they struggled to start the vehicle, Mireles rested his pump shotgun on the bumper of a nearby car and fired. It was pure agony for him, using only one arm. After he fired one round, he had to roll back against the car, stick the shotgun between his legs, and "rack" it with his good right arm. Still, Mireles managed to fire five times.

When his ammunition ran out, Mireles dropped the shotgun and felt himself fading. But he knew that the other agents would be run over if the suspects backed out. He drew his .357 Magnum revolver and pushed himself up with his good arm. "Get down! Get down!" yelled another agent. Instead, Mireles moved in on the getaway car, firing away until Platt and Matix lay motionless. Then Mireles collapsed. The shootout had lasted less than four minutes.

One Miami police officer later told Gordon McNeil, "What Mireles did, you can't teach." And William H. Webster, director of the FBI, declared that Mireles "stands for the best in bravery and dedication." He added, "We set very high standards on duty, and his duty called for him to finish the job." In the 78-year history of the FBI, 41 special agents have died in the line of that duty.

Edmundo Mireles, Jr. joined the FBI in 1979, fulfilling a lifelong dream. "I love the job," he says. "I like to arrest fugitives and felons, to get them off the street. In a way, we're kind of like social workers."

He's so eager to get his man that he sometimes calls on his wife, Liz, who is also an FBI special agent. Liz never hesitates to help. While other couples may go out for a game of tennis, Liz and Ed spend their leisure time target-shooting in the Everglades. Since the gun battle, however, Mireles has had little opportunity for family target-shooting. He has undergone two operations to rebuild his arm. But he has no regrets, despite the fact that rehabilitation has been long and painful.

"I was off duty, at home convalescing for seven months, and after that I could have stayed out longer. But I was going crazy at home," Mireles told PARADE in a recent interview. "I asked the boss in Miami if I could come back and answer the phone. I became the night duty supervisor for the Miami office from October '86 to May '87. All I did was work four to midnight, answer complaint calls, man the radio. That gave me time off during the day to go to my numerous doctors' appointments. My last major doctor's appointment was May 1987. I had an appointment almost every day. Most of it was physical therapy; the others were with plastic and orthopedic surgeons. My last operation was May 1987."

Mireles says his arm is officially only 50% of what it was. "But I try not to let it limit me."

Mireles was transferred to the FBI Academy in Quantico, Virginia, as a supervisor for the new recruits. After two and a half years there, he was ready to return to the streets. "I had to do a lot of talking, a lot of convincing, to get my superiors to let me back on the street," he says. "In September 1989, I was transferred back to Miami at our request. The biggest thing that the Bureau had a question about wasn't my physical ability, it was my mental condition. My wife, Liz, and I had to justify why we wanted to come back after such a traumatic incident."

Today Mireles is a field agent on the narcotics squad, and Liz serves in counter-intelligence. Mireles is enjoying his work. "It's quite exciting. It's a little bit different than what I was doing before. Our 'clients' are different, some techniques are different, and the hours are more erratic. But an investigation is still an investigation. Narcotics is one of the biggest problems facing our society today. I'd kind of like to be part of the defense against it. We may be putting our finger in the dike, but I hope I'm contributing."

Law enforcement work is probably tougher now than ever before, Mireles says, because of the money involved in crime, increased numbers of weapons on the street, and changes in society's value system. But Mireles is not afraid—at least not day-to-day.

"Psychologists were afraid that I would get a flashback, but I've found that experience and training and maturity help overcome these problems." Still, the shooting has left its scars. "The loss of two friends has been by far the most difficult part of the incident to get over."

Last summer, Ed Mireles took his ten-year-old son, Marco, to see the site of the shooting. "I want to see what you did," he told his father. At first, Ed made excuses, mostly because of the distance—35 miles. But finally we drove down there, and he was very inquisitive. Somewhere he's managed to piece the whole story together. I tried to protect him from the grisly stuff.

"He kept asking questions, like 'Where were you?' and 'I want you to tell me exactly where you went and what you did.' I had to retrace the whole path for him, and almost give a detailed account of what we did.

"Marco wanted to know where I wrecked my car, and where it was that I got shot, where I fell down, and how much blood I lost. 'Did you lose 50% of your blood?' he asked. It's a boy's view. He wanted to know if the ambulances came, if other police officers were there, and if they put up the strings around the area.''

Ed says Marco was overwhelmed as he tried to digest the information. But clearly the boy understood the real meaning of the event. ''Back in 1988, once in a store in Virginia, I went to purchase a holster, and told the sales clerk my name. 'Oh, you're Ed Mireles, I've heard that name,' the clerk said. Marco said, 'My Dad's a hero.' I said, 'Marco please, let's not get carried away.' But it made him proud. I had really never seen him beam. He was truly beaming with pride.''

As for heroism, Mireles simply sees himself as a lucky member of a team. The real heroes, he says, were Special Agents Grogan and Dove, ''who gave their lives fighting for something they believed. I'm glad to be back. I'm glad to be around. As for heroism, I accept the title, the accolades. But it's difficult to accept all the recognition and rationalize the loss of two friends. It still hits me—four or five years later. It still chokes me up.''

Ed Mireles wants us all to remember the law enforcement officers who gave their lives in the line of duty. ''Those are the guys we should never forget. They were our friends and neighbors and husbands. They put it on the line.'' Like Ed Mireles, they were willing to make the ultimate sacrifice for their neighbor, for community, and for country.

EPILOGUE

You've just met a wonderful cast of characters, a group of unusually courageous and skillful men and women who have distinguished themselves in the field of law enforcement—and lived to tell about it.

Tragically, many law enforcement officers are not so fortunate.

Like Ed Mireles' FBI colleagues who died in the shootout in which he performed so heroically. Like Chicago Police Officer Irma Ruiz, partner of Gregory Jaglowski, who gave her life to protect schoolchildren endangered by a crazed gunman.

Like hundreds of other officers who never thought twice before putting themselves between citizens like you and me—and danger.

In 1990, more than 140 officers died in the line of duty. Over the last 10 years, there have been more than 1,500 officers killed. That's one death approximately every 57 hours. From Secret Service Agents to prison guards, from local cops on the beat to agents of the Drug Enforcement Agency, we hear their stories on the evening news. Perhaps we read about them in our local papers.

We might even see television film footage of their funerals: the massive banks of flowers, the flag-draped casket, the young wife/husband and children, the weeping parents. The law enforcement colleagues doing their very best to keep a stiff upper lip, and often failing. (After all, they're only human, even though most do a superhuman job.)

Perhaps you've been moved as you've watched scenes like these. Perhaps you've even been one of the caring individuals who lined the streets as the funeral procession made its way slowly by, carrying a local hero to his or her final resting place. Perhaps you sent a sympathy card, or wrote a check, or made a casserole to help the officer's survivors make it through the toughest time in their lives. Or perhaps, like most of us, you thought about doing these things, but did not do them.

Today, you have an opportunity to honor these heroes in a special way—as they have never been honored before. You can help complete the National Law Enforcement Officers Memorial in Washington, D.C., by returning the page at the end of this book, or the Reply Memorandum you may have received with the book, with a generous, tax-deductible contribution today.

You can help pay America's debt of honor to those who willingly put their lives on the line to protect us, the 500,000 ordinary Americans whose daily valor is absolutely extraordinary.

If you decide to help build the Memorial, your name will be added to its Roll of Honor, to be housed permanently as part of the Memorial's Archives. And you will be thought of with warmest gratitude by those in the law enforcement community, especially the families of those who gave their lives in the line of duty.

In a time in which law enforcement officers face more danger than ever before. . .in a time when well-armed drug criminals do not hesitate to "blow away" a policeman. . .your support will truly make a difference. You will be making a positive contribution to the morale of officers who walk those mean streets you and I can choose to avoid. And you will be making an important statement in support of the values that have made America great.

Thank you for reading TOP COPS. I hope I may have the pleasure of hearing from you soon.

> —Craig W. Floyd for
> the National Law Enforcement
> Officers Memorial Fund
> 1360 Beverly Road
> McLean, Virginia 22101

If *You* Want to Say "Thank You" to America's TOP COPS...

Please Return This Coupon With Your Contribution Today!

TO: Craig W. Floyd, Chairman
    National Law Enforcement
      Officers Memorial Fund
    1360 Beverly Road
    McLean, Virginia 22101

☐ YES, Mr. Floyd, I want to help build the National Law Enforcement Officers Memorial, a long-overdue tribute to our fallen law enforcement heroes. Please accept my tax-deductible donation in the following amount:

☐ $100   ☐ $50   ☐$25   ☐$15   ☐Other: $_____

Please keep me updated on the Memorial's construction, dedication, and endowment for the future. Thank you.

Name _____

Address _____

City _____ State _____ Zip _____

Your gift to the National Law Enforcement Officers Memorial Fund is tax-deductible to the fullest extent of the law. Thank you! Of course, you are under no obligation to make a donation or return this reply form.

FEAR STREET®
NIGHTS

Midnight
Games

R.L. STINE

Simon Pulse
New York · London Toronto Sydney

A Parachute Press Book

SIMON PULSE
An imprint of Simon & Schuster Children's Publishing Division
1230 Avenue of the Americas, New York, NY 10020
Copyright © 2005 by Parachute Publishing, L.L.C.
All rights reserved, including the right of reproduction in whole or in part in any form.
SIMON PULSE and colophon are registered trademarks of Simon & Schuster, Inc.
FEAR STREET is a registered trademark of Parachute Press, Inc.
Designed by Sammy Yuen
The text of this book was set in Bembo.
Manufactured in the United States of America
First Simon Pulse edition July 2005
10 9 8 7 6
Library of Congress Control Number 2004118138
ISBN 0-689-87865-6

Part One

1

My friends and I did a horrible thing.

We murdered Candy Shutt, a girl in our class, and then we ran away.

Well, we didn't exactly murder her. It was kind of an accident. But we caused it. We sneaked into her house. We tried to steal a piece of her jewelry. She came after us. She grabbed for it.

We watched her tumble down the stairs. We heard the horrible *crack* her neck made when her head hit the wall. We saw her body sprawled at the bottom of the stairs, so still . . . so unnaturally still . . . her head tilted at such a wrong angle.

We knew Candy was dead. And we ran.

We didn't tell anyone we were there that

night. We kept our secret. Just the three of us—Nikki, Shark, and me.

That was in October. And now it's a month later, and we can't stop thinking about it. Dreaming about it. Talking about it.

Some nights I dream of Candy's big silver pendant with the glowing blue jewels. She called it an *amulet*. I see Candy wearing it, using its evil, casting spells on me and my friends.

And then suddenly, I'm wearing the amulet. And in the dream, I feel all strange, as if I'm outside my body, watching myself, falling into the blue glow of the jewels, surrounded by blue, changing . . . changing into some kind of evil creature . . . changing into some kind of roaring beast. A roaring beast in a tight blue shirt. I'm practically bursting from the shirt. I see red lettering on the front. And I know it's blood. Words scrawled on the shirt in blood. I struggle to read them as the blood pours down the front of the shirt.

And suddenly I can read it clearly. My name?

NATE GARVIN, YOU MURDERED ME!

And I wake up screaming.

Yes, it's happened two or three times. And I have to make up an excuse to my mom, who comes running into my room, her face wide with alarm.

"Nate, why are you screaming in your sleep again?"

I blink my eyes. I can't make the blue glow fade away. It lingers like a fog in front of me. "Uh . . . just a bad dream, I guess. I was dreaming about school."

That's what I tell her.

But of course I was dreaming about Candy. Poor, dead Candy, who fell down the stairs right in front of us. Crack . . . crack . . . *crack*. And that amulet, which we all believed to be so evil.

It's hard to understand if you don't live in Shadyside. If you grew up in Shadyside, you'd know all the stories about the Fear family. They were early settlers of the town. They built a huge mansion on the street named after them—Fear Street.

People claim they were evil. The Fears used the dark arts and evil sorcery to get their way—and to entertain themselves. Weird howls and screams of horror were heard coming from the

Fear Mansion day and night. When we were kids, most of us were too frightened to put a foot anywhere near that street.

We even learned about the Fear family in school.

Simon and Angelica Fear were the most evil of them all. Angelica wore a jeweled amulet that she said gave her immortality. She used it to cast spells and put curses on her enemies.

I never believed any of the stories. I don't believe in evil curses or casting spells on people. I always thought the stories about the Fear family were made up.

But when Candy Shutt showed up wearing a silver amulet with blue jewels, bad things started happening to me and my friends.

I know it sounds crazy. But we became convinced she had found Angelica Fear's amulet. And that she was using it against us.

So we sneaked into her house and tried to steal it.

And that's when the accident happened. That's when Candy fell to her death.

We were left standing there holding her amulet. The evil amulet. *Only, it was plastic and glass.*

Yes, a total fake.

Not Angelica Fear's amulet. A cheap copy. With no magical powers. A cheap copy that broke in half, just the way Candy broke.

Candy died for nothing.

Nikki, Shark, and I ran from the house and never told anyone.

But it's a month later, and I wake up screaming.

I know it wasn't my fault. But how can I make the nightmares stop?

2

Some nights it helps to go hang out and talk with my friends. We wait till our parents are asleep. Then we sneak out of our houses and head for Nights, the all-night bar on Fear Street.

We call ourselves the Night People.

I don't know who started it. Maybe Jamie Richards and Lewis Baransky. But now, a whole bunch of us Shadyside High kids sneak out nearly every night.

After midnight in Shadyside, the houses are dark and silent. The streets are empty. Hardly anything moves. The whole world belongs to us.

No one knows about our secret life except Ryland O'Connor, the bartender at Nights. Our parents think we're snug and sound asleep in our beds.

We usually start out at Nights. Then we

wander around town. We don't do much, just hang out. You know. Enjoy the darkness and be together in our secret world.

And now here it is, a cold November night, a tiny crescent moon high in the sky, and I creep out the back door of my house, eager to see my friends.

The wind is blowing the trees, making them shake and rattle. They are dark, trembling shapes behind a curtain of fog.

I have had the nightmare again. This time, a girl was wearing the pendant. I couldn't see her face, but I could hear her whispered words: *"Kill again . . . kill again!"*

I don't think I screamed. But I woke up in a cold sweat. Stood up in a blue haze, as if the pendant were in the room, the glowing blue light floating all around me.

"Kill again!"

So unfair. I didn't kill anyone. Why can't I lose the frightening dreams?

I trot down the driveway to the street, squinting into the low swirls of fog. And I feel the fog inside and out, as if I'm part of it. Not real at all. But smoke floating through smoke.

Whoa. Nate, get a grip, dude.

Don't totally lose it now.

I lower my head and jog a couple of blocks. Nights Bar is just a few blocks farther. No people in sight, but everything is in motion. The wind bends the grass and sends pebbles dancing along the street.

The fog grows thicker as I turn the corner. I slow to a walk, breathing hard. My breath fogs up in front of me. Fog everywhere.

Candy Shutt's house is on the next block.

I stop. A chill shakes my body. I don't want to go past her house tonight.

The nightmare repeats in my mind, playing out in the fog. I see Candy's dead body, eyes staring blankly up at me.

Why me?

I spin around and start in the other direction. I'll walk through the woods, I decide.

The Fear Street Woods.

The bar is on the other side of the trees, on Fear Street. Actually, Nights stands on the very spot where the Fear Mansion stood.

They tore down the mansion last year. It was a burned-out wreck, anyway. They tore down all the old houses on Fear Street and built a shopping center: Fear Street Acres.

So the street isn't scary anymore. It's filled with cars and bikes and shoppers all day. The Curse of Fear Street is over. At least, that's what they said on all the TV news shows.

I wish I could believe it.

A wall of fog rises up in front of the trees. As if trying to keep me from entering the woods. The trees are old and tangled and tilting one way and the other. But their leaves have fallen, and I can see lights on the other side. The lights of the shopping center.

My shoes crunch on the frosty ground. Dead leaves crackle as I walk along a twisting path. The trees rattle and sigh. I hear an animal scamper through the low shrubs at my right.

I'm about halfway through the stretch of trees. The woods are narrow here. Wisps of fog float in front of me. I trip over a fallen branch and stagger forward to catch my balance.

I brush away a clump of tall reeds and start to walk again. The path has disappeared, but I can see the lights glowing hazily beyond the trees.

I start to walk faster—then I stop. I stop when I hear the hoarse *caw* of a bird. High over my head.

I stop. Another chill tightens the back of my neck.

Everyone knows *there are no birds* in the Fear Street Woods.

That's one of the mysteries of the place.

I raise my eyes to the dark, shivering tree branches. I squint from tree to tree. No sign of it.

Another *caw*—raspy, angry.

And then I see it. A huge blackbird, hunched on a low branch right over my head.

Pale moonlight ripples down through the fog. The light appears to burn the fog away. And, suddenly, I can see the bird clearly.

Its long wings are tucked back, so it appears to be wearing a black cape. I see its long talons curled around the branch. I see its curled bill.

It stares at me with a bright, blue eye. Then the bird tilts its head, and I see the other eye. Black? No. An empty socket. Just a dark hole where the eye should be.

I take a stumbling step back.

Why does it stare at me so intently?

We have a short staring match. The blue eye peering down at me, locked on my eyes.

And then the ugly, one-eyed bird raises its head. It lets out a terrifying cry—a high scream that echoes off the bare trees.

Before I can move, it dives off the branch and swoops down at me, pointed talons raised to attack, screeching in fury.

3

The big blackbird lands heavily. I let out a startled cry as its talons dig into the shoulders of my coat.

It beats its heavy wings against my face. It opens its bill in another screech.

I stumble back against a tree. I raise both hands to protect myself.

Its talons dig deeper into my shoulders. I feel the sharp point of its bill scrape the side of my face. The wings pound harder.

I swing my arms. Grab frantically at its fat body. My hands slide off the coarse feathers.

"Owww!" I scream in pain as the bird lowers its bill to my face. Pecks at my eyes.

I twist my head away. Shoving it. Pushing at it.

The wings flap and scrape my face. The

ugly bird grips me tightly, holding on so it can attack. Again. Again.

I feel hot blood pouring down my cheeks.

"Get off! Get OFF!" I scream.

I stare into the empty eye socket. I can see torn veins and muscles deep inside, as if the eye had been *ripped* out of its head.

Another shrill screech of attack rings in my ears.

I feel dizzy.

This isn't happening. This *can't* be happening.

No way I'm being attacked by a one-eyed bird in the middle of the night in the Fear Street Woods.

But it *is* happening.

And I can't fight the bird off. Too strong. Too heavy and strong.

And angry.

I bat at the bird with both hands. Swing at it, twisting my body, ducking my head.

It scrapes my face again. I feel its sharp bill dig into my skin. Blood pours down both cheeks, from my forehead, over my eyes.

Can't see.

Can't see through the flowing blood.

I drop to the ground beneath the beating wings.

I drop to my knees and struggle to cover my head.

But I feel the pinch of pain as it digs its talons into the back of my neck.

It attacks again. Again.

I'm whimpering now. Covering my head with both hands.

Helpless as it lowers its head to attack again.

"Get off! Get OFF!"

Helpless.

Is it going to kill me?

4

How long was I in the woods? What happened to me there? Why do I have streaks of caked blood on my jacket?

I can't answer those questions.

I feel dazed and shaken. And every part of my body hurts. But I can't answer any questions.

I pull open the door of Nights Bar and smell that familiar beery aroma. I blink a few times, letting my eyes adjust to the low lights.

I squint at the yellow neon Budweiser sign behind the long bar at the front. It says: one-thirty.

I step up to the bar and call to the bartender, Ryland O'Connor, who doesn't pick up his head from the *Biker* magazine he is reading.

Ryland is a tall, stocky, red-faced guy, with spiky blond hair, a silver ring in one ear, and crinkled-up eyes that always seem to be laughing. He has three tiny, blue stars tattooed on his right temple. And a long scar on one cheek that he won't tell anyone how he got.

"Hey, Ry," I say, my voice hoarse. "I really need a beer."

He slowly gazes up at me. "Aren't you forgetting something?"

I blink. "Oh, yeah. For sure."

I back up and kiss the brass plaque on the wall by the front door.

The plaque shows the two original Fears—Angelica and Simon—just their faces, young faces, like they're in their twenties or maybe thirties. Underneath, it says, FIRST SETTLERS OF SHADYSIDE. FEAR MANSION BUILT ON THIS SPOT IN 1889.

We all kiss the plaque when we come into Nights. I mean, just about everyone kisses it. Partly as a joke, and maybe some of us think it keeps bad luck away. I'm not so sure. My friend Galen kissed it one night and his lips got stuck to it. It was horrible. He wound up in the hospital. The weird thing is it happened right after he told me he knew something really important about the Fears. Something dangerous! But I kiss it, anyway.

Ryland slides a bottle of Bud across the bar to me. He knows none of us Night People are old enough. He knows we all have fake IDs. But he's cool about it.

I tilt the bottle to my mouth and take a long pull. My neck aches. All of my muscles ache, as if I've been in an accident or something.

I turn and take a few steps beyond the bar. I see my buddy Shark sitting with Lewis Baransky in a booth against the back wall.

"Hey, Nate—" Jamie Richards calls to me. She's at a table with Ada, my girlfriend. It seems weird to call Ada that. We've only been going out a few weeks. It just sort of happened. I'm not really sure how.

We've been friends for a long time. And then, suddenly . . . wow.

I walk over to Jamie and Ada. I lean down and kiss Ada on the lips. She raises her hands to my face—then jerks them away.

She stares at me wide-eyed. "Nate—what happened to you?"

"Huh? What do you mean?"

Both girls are staring at me now. I drop down in the chair next to Ada.

"Your face—," Ada says. "Is that blood?"

I raise a hand to my cheek. It feels crusty. It hurts when I touch it.

Ada reaches her hand into my hair. "Oh, gross." She makes a disgusted face. "Dried blood. In your hair."

Jamie frowns at me. "What happened? Are you okay? Were you in an accident?"

I shut my eyes to think about it. I have a hollow feeling in my stomach. And my brain . . . my mind is a blank.

"You're totally scratched up, Nate," Ada says, grabbing my hand. "Look. There's blood on your hands, too."

"Hey, Nate—you get in a fight?" Shark calls from the back. "Who won?"

"Definitely not me," I shout back.

But I don't feel like joking around. My ears are ringing. I take another long pull on the beer bottle.

Ada and Jamie are still staring at me. Ada brushes some caked blood off my hair.

"I walked here," I say, thinking hard. "Through Fear Woods. I . . . uh . . . think I fell."

"Did you land on your head?" Shark calls.

Lewis laughs. He has a high whinny of a laugh. He sounds like a horse.

I make a fist. "I'm going to land on *your* head!" I tell Shark.

Shark jumps to his feet. He sneers at me like he's tough or something. "Dude, you want to take it outside?"

I jump to my feet.

Everyone laughs. They know Shark and I are good buddies. Shark is a pretty wild kid. He gets in trouble sometimes. But he'd never fight me. We look out for each other.

Especially since that night at Candy's house. Especially since we have that big, awful secret to keep.

Ada pulls me back down. "So you were walking here and you fell?"

I nod. "Yeah. I guess I cut myself on some brambles."

She shakes her head. "Must be really tough brambles," she mutters. "You're a total mess."

Ada pulls me up and leads me by the hand to the bathroom at the back of the bar. It's a filthy mess. The sink is rusted brown, and there are clumps of wet toilet paper all over the floor.

"Doesn't Ryland ever clean this place?" Ada asks.

I shrug. "He's got a tough job. You know. Sitting up front and reading magazines all night."

Ada wets some paper towels and starts to mop the dried blood off my face. It really hurts, but I don't flinch or anything. Gotta be tough, right?

She frowns at me as she dabs at my cheek. "You sure you fell?"

I hesitate. I almost tell her the truth. That I don't remember how it happened.

But that's just too weird. When I think about how my mind is blank, I get that scared, hollow feeling in my stomach again.

"Yeah. Fell," I said. "Stupid, huh?"

"Yeah," she agrees. "Stupid."

We kiss for a while. I put my arms around her and hold her tight. I want to hold on to her for a long time. Something scary happened to me in the woods, and I don't know what it was.

I only know I'm really afraid.

After a long while, Ada pulls away from me. We're both breathing hard. I can still taste her lips on my lips.

"Let's get out of here," she says, pressing her forehead against mine. "It reeks."

When we return to the table, Shark and Lewis have joined us. Lewis is holding hands with Jamie. They've been going out for years. Shark is spinning a large gold coin around on the table.

"Is that real gold?" Jamie asks. "Where'd you get it?"

Shark holds the coin up for her to see. "It's very old. Know where I got it? That night we were all in the Fear Mansion last year. In that hidden room we found. Before they tore the house down. That night we swiped all that stuff?"

Jamie took the coin and examined it, turning it over. "I'll bet it's real gold."

Shark grinned at her. "Maybe I'm filthy rich and don't know it. I took a whole pile of these coins from that room."

Jamie spins it on the table. Shark grabs it up. He finishes his beer and walks over to Ryland to get another one.

Lewis is wearing his down parka, even though it's about eighty degrees in the bar. He turns to me. "You look tense, Nate."

I don't answer. I don't know what to say to that.

"We're all tense," Ada says. "Everyone at school is tense. Haven't you noticed?"

I tilt the beer bottle to my mouth. "Because of Candy?"

Ada nods. "A lot of people think it wasn't an accident. They think Candy was murdered."

Whoa. I nearly drop the bottle. Shark and I were there. We *know* what happened. We *saw* Candy go flying headfirst down the stairs, screaming to her death.

Shark glances at me. He tucks the gold coin into his jeans pocket. "People think there is a killer out there?"

Ada narrows her eyes at him. "They say it wasn't a human killer. They say it was the curse of Fear Street."

I shake my head. "That's so over," I say. "Fear Street is a shopping center now. How can anyone still believe that stuff?"

Shark taps the table. "We're sitting right where the Fear Mansion stood." He shouts to Ryland behind the bar. "Hey, Ry—think this bar is haunted?"

"Yeah. By you guys." Ryland doesn't lift his head from his magazine.

"Hey, you love us," Shark replies. "If we didn't come here every night, what would you do?"

Ryland grins. "Enjoy the peace and quiet?"

The front door swings open. We all turn. A girl steps into the neon red light at the entrance.

The red light shimmers and wraps around her like a cloak.

And behind the curtain of red, I see . . . I see another figure. A dark figure rising above the girl.

I lean over the table and squint into the eerie light. It's a bird. A giant blackbird. It raises its wings and beats them hard, as if fighting off the red light.

I see one blue eye. The eye seems to be staring into the bar, staring straight at *me*!

I know it.

I recognize that bird from somewhere.

And I open my mouth in a scream I can't stop.

5

Ada jumps up. She shakes me by the shoulders. "Nate—what's wrong? What *is* it?"

The girl takes a few steps into the bar. Behind her, the bird vanishes.

It just disappears into the red neon. The last thing I see is its blue eye.

I take a deep breath and hold it. I watch the girl approach. Did she know that bird was hovering above her? I don't think so.

Ada squeezes my shoulders. "You're trembling," she says. "What made you scream like that?"

Everyone stares at me.

I keep my eyes on the girl. "I . . . I guess I freaked because of that girl," I tell them.

I don't want them to know I'm suddenly seeing strange, one-eyed blackbirds.

"The girl looks so much like Jamie," I say. "I . . . I thought I was seeing double."

Jamie laughs. "Of *course* she looks like me. What's your problem, Nate?" She gives me a gentle shove. "It's my cousin Dana. Remember I told you about her?"

My heart is still pounding.

Up at the front, Ryland is telling Jamie's cousin to kiss the plaque on the wall. She hesitates. She waves at Jamie. Then she leans forward and gives the plaque a peck.

"Remember?" Jamie whispers. "Dana is going to live with me and my family. For the rest of senior year."

I'm starting to feel normal again. But I can't lose the picture of that staring blackbird, floating in the red neon above Dana's head.

"She looks so much like you," I tell Jamie. "Isn't she the one you don't like?"

"Sshhh." Jamie shoves me again. "Here she comes." She turns to the others. "Be nice to her, guys. She's had a horrible year."

Dana steps up to the table. She has Jamie's wavy, black hair and her round, high forehead and dark eyes. When she smiles, she has Jamie's smile.

"Hi, everyone," she says.

"You made it. I didn't know if you were coming or not," Jamie tells her.

Shark pulls over a chair. "I'm Shark," he says. "That's Lewis, and that ugly dude is my friend Nate."

Everyone laughs.

Dana pulls out the chair and starts to sit down.

"Nice to meet you," she says. "I'm Dana Fear."

PART TWO

6

My name is Dana Fear, and I'm seventeen. A week after I moved in with my cousin Jamie Richards, she threw a party to introduce me to her friends. That was very nice of her.

Jamie hasn't always been nice to me.

We didn't get along when we were kids. My first memories are of Jamie pulling my hair and not letting me play with her dolls.

She had shelves and shelves of dolls, I remember. And a big, clean room, with bunk beds so she could have sleepovers. And she had a huge closet filled with toys and games and videos.

My room at home was about the size of her closet. My family was poor, and we lived in a tiny, falling-down house on the edge of the Fear Street Woods.

Jamie's family never visited our house. We always went to her house. Her father was a lawyer or something, and my parents were always talking about how rich they were.

They lived in a big, stone house in North Hills, the fancy part of Shadyside. I remember the long driveway that curved around to the back. They had a barbecue grill with a tall chimney built right into their patio, and their own tennis court.

Funny, the things you remember from your childhood.

I remember standing with Jamie on her tennis court one day. She spilled out a big, wire basket of tennis balls. They rolled all over, and she ordered me to pick them up.

I ran around the court, gathering up tennis balls. And when I filled the basket, she spilled them all out again.

She thought that was a riot. She tossed back her head and laughed. I thought she was really mean.

When I was ten, my family moved away from Shadyside, and I didn't see Jamie for the longest time.

Last year, I heard about her accident. I

didn't know the details. I heard she was at the old Fear Mansion when it was torn down, and she and her friend Lewis fell into the hole for the new foundation. A mountain of dirt started to fall in on them, and they were almost buried alive.

I called Jamie when she finally got home from the hospital. She was surprised to hear from me. She said she couldn't remember the accident at all. She knew that two off-duty cops had rescued her and her friend Lewis.

She said she had a bad hip, which made her limp. But everything else seemed okay. She was totally bummed that she had spent so much time in the hospital in rehab for her leg that she wouldn't be able to graduate with her class. She had to do senior year over again.

We talked on the phone about seeing each other someday, even though we were in different cities. Of course I didn't know then that my life was about to blow up, and that I'd have to come live with Jamie and her parents for the rest of senior year.

Last week, when I climbed the steps of her front porch, I set down my suitcases and my hamster cage, and I took a deep breath before ringing the bell.

I had a heavy feeling in the pit of my stomach.

What would Jamie be like? I wondered. I knew she'd still be pretty, with those big, dark eyes and her creamy, pale skin and wavy, black hair.

But would she be glad to see me? Or would she still treat me as the poor cousin she was forced to hang out with?

I raised my finger to the big, brass doorbell—and the door swung open before I could ring it.

Jamie came rushing out and swept me up in a warm hug. She stepped back to look at me. Then hugged me again.

"You look so fabulous!" she gushed. "I—I can't believe you're here! It's so awesome you're going to be living here!"

She picked up my heaviest bag. "You're tall now," she said. "I was always taller than you, wasn't I? I remember those awful yellow Reeboks you used to wear, without any laces, right? You thought that was cool or something, but it was so geeky."

I laughed. "I didn't think you'd remember me at all."

She narrowed those dark eyes at me. "Of course, I do. I remember everything. I was bossy then, totally mean to you. I guess it was because you were so quiet and sad-looking and . . . shy."

"I'm not shy anymore," I said, grinning.

It's true. No one would ever call me shy. For one thing, I'm really into guys. And I know how to get their attention.

I may not be as pretty and dramatic-looking as Jamie. But guys think I'm hot.

I like to go out and party and get trashed and get crazy.

It helps me forget how sick my life is.

Wow. When Jamie greeted me like that—like a long-lost friend—it meant so much to me. I thought I'd burst out crying. I really did.

I need Jamie to be my friend. My life has sucked for so long. I need this new start. New friends. New *everything*.

I picked up the hamster cage and peered inside. Hammy sat in a corner, burrowed down in the wood shavings, staring out at me with those shiny, black eyes.

I knew he was confused, moving to a new home. Well . . . I was confused too. Confused and hurt and angry.

I picked up my other suitcase and waited

for Jamie to lead the way. She wore an oversize, white T-shirt pulled down over black yoga pants. Her hair fell in loose strands around her face, tied in a single ponytail.

Her skin was paler than I remembered. When she smiled at me, I could see tiny, blue veins pulsing in her temples.

She limped badly as she led the way to the front stairs. I realized she was still not fully recovered from her accident.

I wanted to ask her a million questions about it. What were she and Lewis doing at the wreck of the Fear Mansion? How could they ever fall into such a deep hole? Why were they there so late at night?

The questions could wait. Maybe Jamie didn't even remember the answers.

I followed her up the front stairway. "Dana, you have the whole attic to yourself," she said. "It's very cozy. I think you'll like it. Is that a hamster in there? Better keep him away from my mom. She's allergic to all kinds of animals. What's his name?"

"Hammy," I said. "Clever, huh?"

She laughed. "How did you ever come up with that?"

We were both breathless by the time we dropped the suitcases to the floor in my new attic room. I set the hamster cage down on a table in front of the window. Gazing out, I could see the long, front lawn with its two flower beds, empty now since it was November. Two tall, old trees stood on both sides of the driveway, mostly bare except for a few clumps of dead, brown leaves.

Jamie lifted one of the suitcases onto the narrow bed against the wall. "Sorry about your mom," she said.

"Yeah, sorry," I muttered. "Sorry, sorry, sorry."

She wasn't expecting me to be so bitter. I could see the shock on her face.

"Such a bad year for our family," she said softly. "First, cousin Cindy died, then your mom. How is your dad doing? Your mom died so suddenly. He must still be in shock."

"How should I know?" I asked. My voice trembled. I didn't want it to. I wanted to sound calm and controlled. But sometimes I just can't hold in my anger.

"He won't talk to me," I said. "He can't deal with me, I guess."

Jamie put a hand on my shoulder. "Just because he sent you to live here . . ."

"He didn't *want* me!" I cried. "He didn't want me to live with him. My mom dies. So he sends me off to a cousin I haven't seen in seven years. How should that make me feel? You tell me, Jamie. How should I feel about that?"

I was talking through gritted teeth. I looked down and saw my hands coiled into tight, red fists.

Jamie took a step back. Her face went even paler. I could see she was surprised. She studied me for a long moment.

"Dana, you're scaring me," she said. "I'm serious. You look so angry, like you could kill someone."

Kill someone?

No way. What a strange thing to say.

Did I really look like that?

Kill someone?

Me?

7

It was an excellent party. Jamie had the music cranked up. And the dining room table was loaded down with pepperoni and onion pizzas and long submarine sandwiches.

No beer. Jamie's parents were home. But everyone seemed to be having a good time, anyway.

Danny, Jamie's seven-year-old brother, printed out a banner on his computer: WELCOME, DANA—each letter in a different color. It was strung up over the piano.

Danny is a cool little guy. He has short, blond hair and bright, blue eyes, and a killer smile, even with two front teeth missing. Tonight, he had a fake tattoo of a dragon on one cheek.

Everyone was making a fuss over him. One

of Jamie's friends was trying to teach him how to dance. But he kept stomping down on her feet. He thought that was a riot. Each time he did it, he giggled like a fiend.

The first two guys I bumped into at Jamie's party were Nate and Shark. I'd met them a few nights before at the bar everyone goes to late at night.

Shark told me his real name is Bart Sharkman but everyone calls him Shark. He is a big, athletic-looking guy, kinda intense, nervous. He kept gazing around a lot. I think it was hard for him to stand still for very long.

He is cute. I like his spiky hair. I wondered if maybe I could get the shark to bite. But then this streaky-blond girl named Nikki came over to us and wrapped her arm through Shark's.

Nikki seemed okay. She had a funny sense of humor and a hoarse, smoky voice that I liked.

Nate was kinda cute too. Sort of a cuddly teddy bear type. I knew right away why I could be into him. He reminded me of Dustin, my old boyfriend. No joke. He reminded me of Dustin big-time. So in a way, I kinda felt I already knew Nate.

He had a great laugh. I was teasing him about something and we were having a nice talk. And I guess I had my hand on his shoulder—you know, just being friendly—when this skinny, red-haired girl practically bumps me out of the way.

Jamie hurried over and introduced us. She said the girl's name was Ada Something. I didn't catch the last name. I'd met Ada at the bar the other night, but we didn't get to talk.

Sometimes you get a flash about someone. I mean, I don't really believe in first impressions. But tonight I could see that I probably wasn't going to like this girl Ada.

Just a hunch.

I went to get a Coke from the cooler, and when I turned around, Ada was all over Nate. I mean, I'm not against Public Displays of Affection, but I think she was making a point here, staking out territory, if you know what I mean.

I was just talking to the guy, after all.

I guess maybe I was too intense, standing there staring at them. Because another girl came over and pulled me aside. She was tall and very pretty in a cold sort of way. She had perfect, creamy skin and long, billowy blond hair.

She said her name was Whitney. And she held on to my arm and started talking about Ada and Nate, in a loud whisper. "Ada had a crush on Nate for years," she told me. "But he always looked through her like Saran Wrap or something."

Saran Wrap? *Excuse me?*

"Anyway, after Candy Shutt died, Nate was totally messed up," Whitney continued. "I'm not sure why. I mean, he didn't even *like* Candy. I guess it was the idea of someone we knew, someone in our class dying like that.

"Anyway, Ada tried hard to get him to snap out of it. And they finally started going out."

"And now it's a serious thing?" I said, watching the two of them lip-locked on the couch.

Whitney nodded. Her hair fell over her face, and she brushed it away. "Yeah. Ada is really intense about Nate." She raised her eyes to mine. "I just thought I should warn you. You know."

"Look, I was just talking to him," I said. I don't know why I snapped at her. She just annoyed me. "Are you really trying to tell me I can't talk to some guy without permission? Tell your friend Ada to chill—okay?"

Whitney let go of my arm and stepped back. She couldn't hide her shock from her face. She turned bright red. "I . . . was only trying to help."

"Sorry," I said quickly. "Please. I'm kinda in a haze or something. I didn't mean that. It's been really tough. Losing my mom and . . . having to move to a new place senior year."

Whitney tugged at two long strands of her hair, studying me. I guess she accepted my apology, because she said, "How are you and Jamie related?"

I raised my eyes and saw Jamie across the living room, dancing with little Danny. I had to sigh. Jamie was always so graceful and athletic, and now she had that bad limp. She used a cane around the house but quickly hid it away if anyone came over.

"My mom and Jamie's mom were sisters," I said.

Whitney kept studying me. "So your dad is a Fear?"

I nodded.

"That means Jamie *isn't* a Fear?" Whitney asked.

I laughed. "Are you worried about her? Worried it might be catching or something?"

Whitney blushed again.

Why was I being so nasty? Jamie throws a party for me, and what do I do? Make sure all her friends hate me.

But I knew kids were staring at me because I'm related to the Fear family. I'm not a paranoid nut. I don't think people are staring at me all the time.

But Jamie's friends were definitely checking me out. And not just because of my short skirt and glittery, tight-fitting midriff top.

As the party went on, I overheard kids talking about the Fear family. And the Curse of Fear Street. Sometimes they'd hush up when they saw me come by. Sometimes they kept right on talking.

I carried some paper plates into the kitchen and saw a group of kids huddled around the table. They had tense expressions on their faces, and they were talking about Candy, the girl who had died.

"That jeweled thing she wore. It belonged

to Angelica Fear," said a red-haired girl in a jeans jacket and denim skirt. "It was Angelica's evil amulet. She used it to cast spells on people."

A tall, skinny boy snickered. "How do you know that?"

"Galen saw an old photo," the girl replied. "It showed Angelica Fear wearing the same pendant. Galen started to tell people about it, remember? And he ended up in the hospital."

"So you think the amulet got Candy killed?" another girl asked.

The red-haired girl nodded. "Someone murdered Candy and stole the amulet."

"That's way weird," a boy said. "Everyone knows she fell down the stairs. It was an accident."

"Then explain why the police didn't find the amulet anywhere," the girl replied.

The skinny boy scratched his spiky hair. "So you think there's a killer out there? A killer who has an evil amulet that once belonged to the Fear family?"

The red-haired girl didn't answer the question.

I was standing at the sink, eavesdropping. It

took me a few seconds to realize that she was staring at me. They were all staring at me.

And I knew what they were thinking. I saw the suspicious looks on their faces. And even a little fright.

They knew that I'm a Fear. And they knew I'd been listening to their conversation.

I had hoped for a clean start.

I'd had such a bad year, filled with so much sadness and horror.

I'd hoped to leave it behind.

But the cold looks on their faces made my heart sink.

I turned away and hurried from the kitchen. But the question repeated in my mind:

Am I going to be in trouble because of my name *once again*?

8

I made my way back to the living room. A lot more kids had arrived. Their voices rose up over the booming music. Lots of laughter. Some kids were singing some kind of school song, only with dirty lyrics.

Some guys had sneaked in cans of beer, which they tried to hide at their sides. I heard a loud crash. Shattered glass. Someone yelled, "Oops!"

Jamie bumped into me, carrying a tray of plates and glasses. "I have to order more pizza," she said, shaking her head. "I didn't invite all these kids. I don't even *know* some of them."

I laughed. "I just thought you were majorly popular!"

Jamie hurried away. Someone grabbed my arm. I turned to see Nate smiling at me.

"Come on. Let's go outside," he said, shouting over the voices. "We can't talk in here." He gave me a gentle tug.

I glanced around. "Are you sure Ada won't mind?"

His smile faded. "She doesn't own me."

I followed him out the front door. It was a cold, clear night. A tiny sliver of moon was almost lost in a sky full of stars.

Cars jammed the driveway and both sides of the street. One of them was parked on Jamie's front lawn.

Nate shook his head. "Mr. Richards isn't going to be too happy about that."

I hugged myself, trying to stay warm. My little midriff top wasn't much good against the cold. My arms had goosebumps up and down.

Nate appeared tense. He had his eyes down on his sneakers. "Sorry about Ada," he muttered. "I mean, the way she pulled me away like that."

"No problem," I said. I didn't know *what* to say. "How long have you been together?" I asked.

He shrugged in reply. "I'm not even sure we *are* going together."

"Liar," I said, grinning. "That's not what I heard."

He grinned back.

I guessed he was interested in me. Maybe *very* interested.

I didn't mind. I was interested in him, too. I thought, maybe he'd like to put his arms around me and warm me up.

But he didn't make a move. He just stood there, staring down at the ground. "Hey, maybe you and I could hang out or something," he said finally.

"Cool," I said.

Then he ruined it. He raised his eyes to mine and said, "I've always wanted to meet a Fear."

"Really?" Is that why he's so interested?

"I have a lot of questions," he said. "You know. About your family."

Well, that was nice while it lasted.

I thought he wanted me—not my family.

"You writing a magazine article?" I snapped. I didn't mean it to sound so cold, but it did.

Nate didn't seem to notice. He jammed his hands into his jeans pockets. "No. Things have been weird around here. I mean, some scary things happened to my friends and me. Like we were cursed or something. We almost drowned, you know. And then that girl in our class died. . . ."

His voice trailed off. I could see he was really messed up. But why did he think I had anything helpful to tell him?

I was shivering. I rubbed my arms. "Think I have to go inside," I said.

I turned—and saw a face pressed against the window, staring out. Ada. She was glaring at Nate and me.

Was she bad news or what?

"Look, Nate—," I started.

But he had turned away from me. He was staring up into the branches of a tall sycamore tree.

"Earth calling Nate," I said. "What's up there?"

"A bird," he said. He turned back to me, scratching his head. "I thought I saw a black-bird. I mean. Well . . . I guess it was just a shadow."

"You're into bird watching?" I said.

He didn't seem to hear me.

Ada still had her face pressed to the window glass. I decided to give her something to look at. I slid my arm around Nate's shoulders, pulled him close, and led him back into the house.

Jamie greeted me at the door. She squinted at me. "You and Nate?"

"Just talking," I said. "It's hard to hear in here."

"I need you," Jamie said, pulling me through the crowded living room. "I'm out of everything. Some guys went for pizza. Can you check the basement? See if you can find any more cans of Coke?"

"No problem," I said. I shivered. I couldn't shake off the cold from outside. "Just let me run up to my room and put on something warmer."

I bumped past Lewis, who was changing the CDs on the music system. Two couples were pressed together at the bottom of the stairs. They squirmed to the side so I could get upstairs.

I found a long-sleeved pullover in my dresser, tugged it on, and hurried back to help cousin Jamie. I stopped at the landing because someone was blocking the way.

Ada stood in front of me on the top step. She held a tray of glasses in front of her. The glasses tinkled as the tray shook in Ada's hands.

The bright ceiling light reflected off the glass, and I blinked. Whoa.

I suddenly felt dizzy, off-balance. The floor tilted, and the stairs appeared to rise up in front of me.

What a strange feeling. Why was the light reflecting so brightly? White light. Almost blinding.

I shut my eyes for a moment, trying to fight off the dizziness.

I opened them when I heard a shrill scream—and saw Ada falling . . . Ada tumbling . . . toppling headfirst down the staircase.

9

Screaming all the way, Ada thudded down the stairs.

The music and voices were so loud, but I could hear every *bump*, every time her head hit a wooden step.

And then the voices and singing and laughter stopped. As if someone had turned a switch. A few seconds after that, the music stopped too.

And now I felt as if I were swimming in silence, an ocean of silence. A bright white ocean of silence and light.

I grabbed the banister. I peered down through the billowing whiteness, forcing my eyes to focus.

And saw Ada. Crumpled up. Sprawled in a heap, surrounded by glittering lights. It took me a while to realize the lights were pieces of broken glass.

"Is she okay?" I screamed into the silence.

Kids were rushing to the stairway now, dropping down beside Ada. Brushing away the shards of shattered glass. Reaching for her. Eyes wide with worry and amazement.

Ada groaned. She slowly pushed herself up to a sitting position.

I saw bright red blood streaming down the front of her T-shirt and staining one sleeve. Bits of broken glass shimmered in her hair.

She groaned again and wiped her hands through her hair. Then, slowly, she raised her eyes to me.

I gasped when I saw the fierce anger on her face.

"You PUSHED me!" Ada screamed.

I heard gasps and low cries. All eyes were raised to me.

My legs felt wobbly, about to give way. I gripped the banister tightly to hold myself up. I felt my heart start to pound.

"N-no," I stammered, shaking my head. "I didn't touch you!"

Ada raised herself to her knees. She shook

a blood-smeared fist at me. "You DID, Dana!" she cried. "You shoved me!"

I couldn't help it. I burst into tears. "That's a LIE!" I cried. But my sobs muffled the words.

I gazed down from face to face. They all stared at me, accusing me. They *believed* her.

But I knew it wasn't true. I never touched her.

Why was she accusing me?

I couldn't stop sobbing. I turned and ran up the stairs. Back to my attic room, where I dropped into an armchair. I gripped the arms hard, gritted my teeth, and forced myself to stop crying.

From my room I could hear voices downstairs. But I couldn't make out the words. Were they all talking about me? Did they all believe Ada?

Why would I push her down the stairs? I had no reason to hurt her.

Did they think I pushed her because I want to steal Nate?

Nate is cute, but he isn't worth trying to *kill* someone!

Did they think I pushed her because I'm a Fear? And a member of the Fear family *has* to be evil? How stupid is *that*?

I heard the front door close. Heard voices in the driveway. Car doors slammed, and engines started up. The party was breaking up.

I was still hunched in the armchair, gritting my teeth, thinking angry thoughts, when Jamie came into my room. She hurried over and placed a hand on mine. "Dana, are you okay?"

"I . . . don't know," I said. I felt like crying again, but I forced it back.

Jamie squeezed my hand. "It was a good party," she said softly, "until Ada fell."

"I didn't push her!" I cried. I jerked Jamie's hand off mine. "Really. I never touched her."

Jamie nodded. "Of course you didn't."

I jumped to my feet. I balled my hands into tight fists. "So why did she accuse me like that?"

Jamie tossed back her dark hair. She suddenly looked so pale and tired. I could see that blue vein throbbing in her temple. "Ada will get over it," she said.

"Get over it?" I cried. "How? If she thinks I tried to kill her . . ."

"She was being emotional," Jamie replied. "Ada is very high-strung. When she thinks about it, she'll realize she made a mistake. She tripped, that's all."

"I . . . I felt weird up there," I confessed. "I was standing behind Ada at the top of the stairs. And the glasses on her tray suddenly started to shine in my eyes. I felt dizzy."

"Dizzy?"

"Yes. I thought I might black out. But . . . you've got to believe me. I didn't push her. I couldn't."

"Of course not," Jamie said in a soft, soothing voice. "Of course not."

So why was she staring at me so suspiciously?

10

The next couple of days I kept to myself. I was eager to find out what kind of greeting I'd get from everyone my first day at Shadyside High. But the school was closed for two days because of a water-main break.

Jamie hung out with Lewis and some of her other friends. And I heard her sneaking out after midnight to see her friends at the bar they all go to on Fear Street.

But I didn't feel like tagging along. Well, I guess I was a *little* tempted. I wanted to see Nate again. I kept thinking about him without even realizing it.

I wondered if he believed I pushed Ada down the stairs. I wondered if he'd be glad to see me, or if he'd try to avoid me.

But I didn't leave the house. I e-mailed

some friends from my old school. And I called my dad. Told him everything was just great. (As if he cared.) And I tried to read ahead in some of the school assignments.

The night before the high school was to open again, Jamie appeared in my room. "What's up?"

"Not much," I said. "Reading this Shakespeare play for English." I held up the book.

Jamie straightened some papers on my desk. "You nervous about tomorrow?"

"Kinda," I replied. "I'm sure your friends all think I'm some kind of monster because I'm a Fear and they think I pushed Ada down the stairs."

"No way," Jamie said, shaking her head. "No one is even talking about that anymore."

A lie. But a nice lie.

I couldn't get over the change in Jamie. How she was trying so hard to make me feel comfortable and everything.

Then she mentioned our cousin Cindy.

Cindy died in the hospital last August. She had been sick for a long time, but it was horrible and shocking. She was just a year older than Jamie and me.

"I saw Cindy a week before she died," Jamie said, settling on the edge of my bed. "Did you see her?"

"No. I was too far away," I replied, putting down my book. "But I talked to her on the phone. She . . . she said she was getting stronger. I knew she was just being brave."

I sighed. "She died three days later. When I heard, I cried and cried. She was such a cool person."

Jamie's eyes narrowed. She had a cold expression on her face, an expression I'd never seen before. "Life can really suck," she whispered.

We stared at each other for a long moment. My ears started to ring. I waited for Jamie to break the silence. When she didn't, I said, "You know, Cindy was a Fear too."

A strange smile spread over Jamie's lips. "I know." She picked at the strings around the hole on the knee of her jeans. "Dana, did Cindy say anything to you about sending a signal?"

I narrowed my eyes at her. "A signal? No."

Jamie tugged at the knee of her jeans. "Cindy promised me she'd send a signal," she said, her voice just above a whisper.

It took me a while to understand. "You mean a signal from the grave?"

Jamie nodded. "She promised. She said she'd send me a sign from the other side. I've been watching for it ever since . . . ever since she died."

I leaned forward in my chair. "And?"

"Nothing yet. But I keep watching. And I keep trying to reach her." Jamie crossed her arms in front of her. "Do you believe in ghosts?"

I laughed. "Because I'm a Fear?"

Jamie didn't smile. "No. Do you believe in spirits?"

"I . . . don't think so," I said. "I mean, I never think about stuff like that."

"I do," Jamie said. "I believe in spirits. I *want* to believe in them. I want to contact Cindy's spirit. I want her promise to come true."

I stared at Jamie. This wasn't like her at all. When I knew her, she was a spoiled rich kid, and kind of a bubblehead. She thought mostly about her hair and boys and buying new clothes. I never knew she was into the supernatural.

"Why?" I asked.

"Because I miss her so much," Jamie said. She jumped to her feet and pulled me up. "Come downstairs."

I followed her down the stairs. I saw flickering lights from her room. Stepping into the doorway, I saw that the room was dark—except for the dancing flames of five candles set up on the floor in a circle. Five black candles.

I hesitated. "Jamie—?"

She shoved me into the room and carefully closed the door behind us. The room smelled spicy, as if she'd been burning incense. The candle flames sent flickering light to the walls, and I saw a giant *Buffy* poster over Jamie's bed.

Jamie motioned for me to sit down in front of the candles. She dropped beside me and sat cross-legged. The orange light flickered and danced over her pale face, her dark eyes glowing with excitement.

"I've been teaching myself magic," she said, staring straight ahead into the firelight.

"You mean to contact Cindy?"

She nodded. She slid an old book out from under her bed. The cover was cracked and torn. She opened it carefully, flipping through the brittle pages.

"I found this old spellbook," she whispered. "I've been trying different spells. I know I can contact her."

I felt a chill tighten the back of my neck. This wasn't like the Jamie I remembered. Cindy's death must have hit her really hard.

"Do your parents know about this?" I asked, staring into the darting orange light.

"Of course not," Jamie whispered. "They never come upstairs."

She ran her finger down a long column of type in the old book. "Dana, we can do it," she said. "Let's try and contact Cindy together."

"Okay," I replied, feeling another chill.

Did I have a choice? She was kinda freaking me out. But *no way* I could jump up and leave.

We held hands. We leaned toward the circle of black candles.

Jamie held the book in her lap. She whispered some words in a language I didn't recognize. Then she began to chant in a loud whisper: "Cindy, where are you? Cindy, where are you . . . ?"

I took a deep breath and joined in. "Cindy, where are you? Cindy, where are you? Cindy, where are you?"

Holding hands, the firelight washing over us, we chanted the phrase over and over. "Cindy, where are you . . . ?"

And then my heart skipped a beat when I heard a soft reply from close by: *"I'm here . . . I'm HERE!"*

11

I raised my eyes to Jamie. She stared back at me, eyes wide, her mouth hanging open. She had heard it too.

I raised myself to my knees. In my excitement, I almost knocked over one of the candles.

"Cindy? Is that you?" Jamie whispered.

And again we heard the soft whisper of a voice, so close . . . so close to us: *"I'm here . . . I'm here."*

I froze, blinking into the flickering flames.

Jamie jumped to her feet. Her eyes narrowed. "Wait a minute," she murmured.

She tiptoed to her closet, pulled open the door—and Danny came tumbling out. "You RAT!" Jamie screamed.

It took me a few seconds to realize that Danny had been the whisperer.

Jamie grabbed the little guy, and he started to giggle. Jamie wrestled him to the floor and tickled his stomach with both hands. He wriggled on his back, giggling and slapping at Jamie.

"You rat! You rat!" Jamie cried, laughing with her brother.

"You scared me to *death*!" I confessed.

Danny rolled out of his sister's grasp. He jumped to his feet and sprinted to the doorway.

"How long were you in there?" Jamie demanded.

He didn't answer. He giggled some more, totally pleased with his little joke. Then he disappeared into the hall. We heard him clumping down the stairs, shouting, "Hey, Mom! Mom! I played a joke on Jamie and Dana!"

Jamie dropped back onto her knees on the carpet and began to blow out the candles. "Guess we won't reach Cindy tonight," she said.

"Think Danny knew what we were doing?" I asked.

She shrugged. "Who knows *what* Danny knows? He's such a funny kid."

"Yeah, funny," I said. My heart was still pounding.

• • •

My first day at Shadyside High was as hard as I'd expected. I mean, how impossible is it to start a new school senior year?

Jamie gave me a short tour of the building before classes started. But of course I forgot everything she told me as soon as she hurried off to homeroom.

I kept staring at faces, looking for kids I knew. I actually remembered some kids from elementary school, but they didn't seem to remember me.

I saw Nate in the hall between third and fourth period. I hurried over to him, but he was rushing somewhere with his friend Shark. We barely said hi.

After school, I found Ada and Whitney in front of their lockers. They were both talking at once. But when they saw me coming, they stopped and both put these fake smiles on their faces.

Whitney wore a short, pleated skirt and layers of T-shirts. Ada had a maroon and gray Shadyside High sweatshirt pulled down over very tight, boot-cut jeans.

"How's it going, Dana?" Whitney asked, eyeing me up and down.

I sighed. "I was late to two classes. I couldn't find the rooms. My school was all on one level, not three floors."

Ada snickered. "Jamie should've drawn you a map."

"I guess," I said. "I'm sure I'll figure it all out in a few days."

Ada shifted her backpack on her shoulders. She was staring at me coldly.

I wanted to apologize for the other night at Jamie's party. I wanted to find out if she still thought I had pushed her down the stairs. I didn't want one of Jamie's friends as an enemy.

But how could I bring it up?

Besides, I was late for an after-school try-out.

"Where is the music room?" I asked them. "I'm totally turned around. I'm supposed to be there now. I'm trying out for chorus."

Ada's mouth dropped open. "Whitney and I are in the chorus," she said. "It's all filled up."

She said it so coldly, as if I had no business even asking her about it.

"My chorus teacher from back home sent a note to Ms. Watson," I explained. "She told her about the singing awards I've won."

"So Ms. Watson said you could try out?" Ada asked.

I nodded. "Yes. She's waiting for me in the music room." I held up both hands with my fingers crossed. "I really need to be in chorus," I told them. "Because I'm trying out for the Collingsworth Music Scholarship."

They both gasped. They exchanged glances. "Ada and I are both trying for the Collingsworth Prize," Whitney said. They glared at me. They didn't even try to hide their feelings.

"I'm sorry," I said. "I guess we'll be competing against one another."

"Guess we will," Ada muttered.

"If I don't win it, I won't be able to go to college," I said. I don't know why I told them that. It was very personal. I guess I was trying to make them my friends.

The Collingsworth Music Scholarship is a statewide scholarship. It includes singing and academics. You have to have a really good grade point average to apply.

I'm a good student, and I know how to get good grades. But sometimes I clutch at test time. I didn't do that well on my SATs.

My singing is the one thing I'm confident

about. I hoped I was good enough to win the scholarship. Otherwise, I'd have to get a job after high school.

Ada and Whitney were still frowning at me. "Only two students can be sent from each high school," Ada said. "We can only send two kids to compete at the state level."

"I know," I said. I didn't know what else to say. Of course it meant that all three of us couldn't win.

I glanced at my watch. "I'm really late," I said. "Can you direct me to the music room?"

They kept staring at me, letting me know they didn't like me. Ada rubbed her shoulder. "It still hurts from the other night," she said. "Something is pulled. I have to have X-rays."

"I'm sorry," I told her. Then I added, "I didn't push you. I would never do anything like that."

She didn't reply to that. Instead, she pointed down the hall. "Keep going that way to the end. You'll find it."

"Thanks," I said. I turned and hurried off.

"Good luck," Whitney called, totally sarcastic.

"Yeah, good luck," Ada shouted. "Break a leg!"

12

The school was emptying. Kids were going home. I jogged down the long hall, dodging a group of cheerleaders carrying silver batons.

I thought about Ada and Whitney. What a shame we'd be competing for the scholarship prize. I realized I'd never win them over as friends.

I could tell they really believed I pushed Ada down those stairs. Is that what *everyone* in school believes?

How unlucky to start out life at Shadyside High with everyone suspecting me. And all because of a misunderstanding.

I tried to force those thoughts from my mind. I had to keep cool and concentrate on impressing Ms. Watson. Making friends was not as important as winning the money to go to college.

Ms. Watson was a tall woman, young and very pretty, with shiny, blue eyes, high cheekbones like a model, and light blond hair pulled back in a French braid. She wore a pale blue turtleneck over tight, charcoal slacks that showed off her long legs.

As I entered, she looked up from her desk, where she was sorting through a stack of sheet music. She had a killer smile. "Are you Dana?"

I nodded. "Yes. Sorry, I'm late. I couldn't find this room."

She crossed the room and shook hands with me. She was at least a head taller than me! I barely came up to her shoulders. "Your first day?" she asked.

"It seems like *ten* days," I replied. "I spent most of the day totally lost."

"Well, come over here." She led the way to her desk. She had a music stand set up beside it. "You certainly come highly recommended. What's-his-name—Mr. Margolis? He couldn't stop praising you in his letter."

"He's really nice," I said. Hearing my old music teacher's name gave me a pang of homesickness.

Ms. Watson picked up the letter from her

desk. "This is an impressive list of singing awards, Dana. Did you bring music with you?"

"No. I have some things memorized," I said. My throat tightened. I suddenly felt cold, nervous. The feeling I always have before singing.

"I have a song from *The Vagabond King*," I told her. "You know. The operetta. And I have a Bach piece we used to use as a warm-up."

"Excellent," Ms. Watson said, flashing me that smile again. I want the name of her teeth-whitener, I thought. She motioned me to the music stand and took a seat behind her desk. "Anytime you're ready, Dana."

I cleared my throat. As I turned to the front of the room, I saw something move in the doorway. The classroom door was open a little more than a crack. I could see a person standing there. And I recognized her by her red hair.

Ada.

Hiding there. Spying on me from the hall.

I took a deep breath. Anger pushed away all my nervousness.

Okay, Ada, I thought. If you want to see a show, I'll give you a show.

I don't think I ever sang better. My voice was clear and steady. I don't think I wavered on a single note. And all the while I could see Ada hunched at the door, eavesdropping on my performance.

When I finished the second piece, Ms. Watson applauded. "Dana, I'm impressed," she said, standing up and shaking my hand again. "Mr. Margolis didn't exaggerate. You really have a gift."

"Thank you," I said. "I've been singing since I was a little girl. My mother heard me singing along with a CD when I was three or something. She couldn't believe I was hitting all the notes. So she started me with lessons."

"You should congratulate your mother," Ms. Watson said. "That was very wise of her."

"I can't," I blurted out. "She died a few months ago."

Ms. Watson's cheeks turned bright pink. "Oh, I'm sorry." She bit her bottom lip. Her bright blue eyes locked on mine.

"Anyway," she said, "we need you desperately in our chorus. I know the others will be so happy to have you join us."

I glanced at the doorway. Ada hadn't

moved. I wondered what she was thinking. Probably making hex signs.

"Thank you," I said. "You'll have to show me what you've been singing. It'll probably take me a while to catch up."

Ms. Watson returned to her desk and sifted through a file of papers. "Dana, have you applied for the Collingsworth Prize? I think I have an application for it here."

"Thank you. I've already filled it out," I told her.

I thought I heard Ada groan from behind the doorway.

"Well, this school is naming two finalists," Ms. Watson said. "I think you have a real chance."

It was my turn to blush. She was being so awesomely nice.

"I'll try," I said.

She handed me a schedule of chorus rehearsals. I thanked her again and strode out of the room. I swung the door open wide.

Ada must have been frozen there or something. She hadn't moved.

Behind me, Ms. Watson let out a startled cry. "Ada? Are you still in school?"

Ada blinked several times, as if coming out of a daze. "Uh . . . yeah. I had to stay after," she said.

"Do you have a minute? I want to talk to you," Ms. Watson said, motioning for Ada to come in. "Have you met Dana?"

Ada didn't look at me. "Yeah. We've met."

"I've got to run," I said. I pushed past Ada and hurried out the door. I pulled the door shut after me—but only partway.

It was *my* turn to eavesdrop!

I gripped the doorknob and stepped back from the opening. I kept glancing up and down the hall, making sure no one was approaching. But it was nearly four o'clock. The hall was empty.

I leaned into the doorway and listened.

"I don't understand," Ada was saying. She didn't sound happy.

Ms. Watson replied in a low, steady voice. "I'm saying you have to bring your singing up to the next level, Ada. Or I'm afraid you won't make the finals."

"But . . ." Ada hesitated. "Ms. Watson, you practically *guaranteed* that I'd go to the state finals."

"Well, I didn't really guarantee it," the teacher replied. "And, I have to be honest with you, Ada. The competition has just gotten a lot tougher."

Silence for a long moment. Then Ada said, "You mean Dana?"

"Yes," Ms. Watson replied. "Dana has had a lot of training. I can't lie: I was impressed by her. She's a very strong singer."

"But that isn't *fair*!" Ada was whining now. "She's too late, isn't she? She can't just transfer here and—"

"Dana is definitely eligible," the teacher replied. "Take it easy, Ada. You're getting yourself all worked up over nothing. You can still qualify. You just have to work hard. Practice a lot more. Concentrate your efforts."

Again, Ada was silent. Then she muttered something too low for me to hear.

She came storming out, shoving the door in front of her. I staggered back. Her face was bright red, and her mouth was set in an angry scowl.

I don't know if she saw me or not. She spun the other way and strode down the hall, her shoes thudding loudly on the concrete floor.

Now I *definitely* have made an enemy, I told myself.

I suddenly pictured Jamie. Jamie and Ada were such good friends. I knew Jamie wouldn't want Ada and me to be at each other's throats.

I decided to go after Ada and talk to her. Tell her I really wanted us to be friends. See if I could convince her to start all over.

I trotted down the long, empty hall. My footsteps echoed against the tile walls and banks of metal lockers.

I turned the corner and gazed down another long hall. No sign of Ada.

How did she disappear so fast? I wondered.

And then I let out a scream as someone grabbed me hard from behind.

13

I spun around. "Nate! What are you doing here?"

He grinned at me. He has a cute, lopsided grin. "Sorry. Didn't mean to scare you."

"Yes, you did," I teased. "You like to make girls scream, don't you?"

His grin grew wider. "Maybe."

"So why are you still here?"

He shrugged. "Shark and I had detention. Don't ask."

I narrowed my eyes at him. "Nate, I thought you were a *good* boy."

He grinned again. "I can be *very* good."

I could see he liked me teasing him like that, coming on to him. Did I have a crush on him already? My mind was spinning.

Stay away from him, Dana. Ada already hates you. Don't make it worse.

"So? What's up?" I asked. I started walking to my locker.

He hurried after me. "These guys . . . uh . . . they're having a skating party Saturday night. On Fear Lake."

Fear Lake. I hadn't thought about that lake on the other side of the woods since I was a kid. My family used to have picnics on the shore. And my dad would drag a canoe there and we'd paddle around for hours.

The memories rushed back to me. Fun times. Before we moved away. Before it all turned bad. . . .

"Is the lake frozen already?" I asked.

Nate nodded. "Yeah. It's been so cold this fall."

"I'm not a great ice-skater," I said. "Weak ankles."

He raised his eyes to mine. "You're probably better than me. The last time Shark and I went skating, I fell on top of a six-year-old girl. It was totally embarrassing."

I laughed. I stopped at my locker. I stared at the lock, trying to remember the combination.

"So . . . you want to go?" Nate asked. "You know. With me?"

I turned back to him. "What about Ada?"

His smile faded. "I *told* you. She doesn't own me." He pulled down the neck of his T-shirt. "See? No leash."

I pictured Ada and Whitney staring at me so coldly. "Well . . ."

"I like you," Nate blurted out. "You're interesting."

"Thanks for the compliment," I said. "Okay. I'll go."

That brought the smile back to his face. But I immediately regretted it.

What did he mean, I was *interesting*?

Was Nate interested in *me*? Or was he interested because he thought I could tell him stories about the Fear family?

I had to talk to Jamie.

I needed advice on what to do about Ada. And I needed advice about Nate.

My first day at Shadyside High, and already I felt in the middle of something. Maybe Nate was someone I could really be into. Maybe he was someone I could trust, someone to rely on.

Or was he someone I should stay away from?

Jamie would tell me.

I hurried home. The sun had already lowered behind the trees. I hate winter. I hate when it gets dark so early.

I looked for Jamie in her room. I saw her backpack and her bag tossed on the floor by her bed, so I knew she was home. But no sign of her.

Jamie's mom—my aunt Audra—was in the den. She looks like an older version of Jamie, with wavy, black hair and creamy, white skin. She had classical music on the stereo. She was lying on the couch, doing a crossword puzzle.

"Jamie is in her studio," she told me. "You know. In the garage. Ever since the accident, that's where she spends her time. Doing pottery she never lets me see."

Did I detect a little bitterness there?

I thanked her and headed to the back of the house.

"Dana, how was your first day?" Aunt Audra called after me.

"Great!" I shouted back. No sense getting into it.

I closed the kitchen door behind me and stepped onto the driveway. A gusting wind had come up, shaking the bare trees in the backyard. A shutter rattled at the side of the house.

I was still wearing my down jacket from school. I pulled up the collar as I trotted to the garage.

The single, pull-down door was shut. The door had no window, but I could see yellow light pouring out at the side of the garage.

"Hey, Jamie!" I shouted, cupping my hands around my mouth. "It's me!" I listened hard. No reply. "Hey—Jamie?"

I bent down, grabbed the garage door handle, and started to hoist up the heavy door.

I had it raised a foot or so from the driveway when I heard the loud shriek from inside:

"Stay OUT! I mean it! STAY OUT!"

14

"Jamie, it's me," I called. "Are you okay?"

I heard running footsteps. The garage door rolled up a few feet. Jamie slid outside and pushed the door down behind her.

Her face was red, and she was breathing hard.

I jumped back. "Sorry. Why did you scream like that? You . . . you scared me."

She had a towel in one hand, covered with brown and red stains. She used it to wipe a spot of clay off one cheek.

"I'm sorry too," she said. "I didn't mean to scream. It's just . . . well . . . I don't allow anyone in my sculpture studio."

I narrowed my eyes at her. "Excuse me?"

"It's kinda my own private space," she said, balling up the towel between her hands. "It's my therapy. After the accident . . . after I fell into that excavation hole last year, I was home for months. I needed a lot of rehab time. I turned this studio into my own private world."

I still didn't understand why I couldn't come in and see what she was doing. But no point in arguing with her. She had a rough year, after all. She's entitled to her own space.

She studied me for a moment. "Dana, how was your first day at our lovely school?"

"Just *lovely*," I said. I grabbed the sleeve of her sweatshirt. "Can I talk to you for a minute or two?"

She nodded. "Sure. Give me a sec to clean up. I'll meet you in the kitchen."

When she joined me at the kitchen table a few minutes later, she still had a spot of red clay on one cheek. She dropped down across from me and rolled up her sweatshirt sleeves.

"You're sweating," I said.

"It's hot in there," she said, mopping her forehead with the back of her hand. "It's the kiln. Dad went a little crazy. He got me the biggest kiln they make, I think. It's like a blast furnace."

She jumped up, jogged to the fridge, and came back with a bottle of water. After downing half the bottle, she turned to me. "So? What's up? Your first day at Shadyside High. Details, please."

I told her about being lost and a little overwhelmed by the size of the place. And I told her about a couple of cute guys I met in the library.

She stuck her finger down her throat and made gagging sounds. "I know those guys. They're not cute once you get to know them."

I laughed. "Yeah, I know they're not the clean-cut, straight-arrow type like Lewis. But I like punky guys."

She shrugged. "Whatever." She brushed her wavy, dark hair off one eye. "So what did you want to talk to me about?"

"Well, I found out something kinda bad after school," I began. I told her about running into Ada and Whitney on my way to my audition with Ms. Watson. And I told her how I'd applied for the Collingsworth Prize.

"Uh-oh," Jamie muttered, squeezing the plastic water bottle in her hand. "Ada and Whitney applied too."

"You got it," I said.

Jamie took another long slug of water, keeping her eyes on me. "Ada has to be furious," she said. "She thinks she has that scholarship prize aced."

"I know," I said. "That's strike two for me with your friend Ada."

Jamie frowned. "Or maybe strike three," she said. "Ada looks like a little mouse, but she has an awesome temper. Red hair, you know."

"I got off to a *horrible* start with Ada," I said. "I know she's your good friend. I don't want her to hate me. But I *have* to win that prize, Jamie."

Her mouth dropped open. I guess I was a little intense.

"Don't you understand? If I don't win that prize," I said, "I'll have to go to work. I won't be able to go to college."

Jamie nodded. "Yeah, I know, Dana."

"I feel bad for Ada," I said. "But I'll do *anything* to win."

Jamie stared hard at me. "Anything?"

"Well . . . ," I replied. "Yeah. Anything."

15

I guess I had a few beers. I was feeling pretty good. I mean, there I was at a table full of guys. It was about one A.M. on Wednesday night, and none of the other girls had come into Nights yet.

I was kicking back, having a nice time, flirting with all of them. Nate had an arm draped over my shoulder. Shark kept pulling out his cell, calling that girl Nikki, asking why she wasn't coming tonight. Lewis and Galen kept tossing popcorn in the air, trying to see who could catch the most in their mouths.

"Who started this idea of sneaking out late at night?" I asked.

"Is it night?" Shark joked. "No wonder it's so dark!" He'd had more beers than I had.

"Jamie and I started it," Lewis said. He was

the only one drinking Diet Cokes. "We called ourselves the Night People."

"Clever name," Galen said. "Did you think of that all by yourself?"

Lewis ignored him. "Jamie and I started sneaking out before this bar was built. We used to meet inside the old Fear Mansion, right on this spot."

Galen rolled his eyes. "Tell us something we *don't* know." He slid out of the booth and walked up to the front to get another beer from Ryland O'Connor.

"Pretty soon these copycats started sneaking out too," Lewis told me. "Jamie and I can't get any privacy."

Shark jabbed Lewis in the ribs. "And why do you need privacy?" he teased.

We all laughed.

"Well, this is so cool," I gushed. "We have secret night lives no one knows about."

Shark leaned into me. "Tell us some secrets, Dana."

"No way," I said, pushing him away.

"Come on. Give us a break. Tell us some dirty secrets." He took a long pull from his beer bottle.

"Shark, you always act like this after half a beer?" I said.

Everyone laughed again, even Ryland from behind the bar.

Galen brought refills for everyone. Nate lowered his hand from my shoulder to take his beer. "So you didn't do this back home?" he asked.

I shook my head. "My parents would have *killed* me. I can't believe your parents haven't found out."

"My parents are divorced," Nate said. "That means I have only *one* parent to fool. And she works all day, so it would take a bomb blast to wake her up."

"My parents drink themselves to sleep," Shark said. "It's not much of a challenge to sneak out."

"Lucky," Galen said.

Lewis kept gazing at the front door. Maybe he was expecting Jamie to show.

Nate squeezed my hand. "So what did you do for laughs back home?"

I shoved his hand away. "None of your business. You're too young."

The other guys hee-hawed at that one.

The five of us kidded around for a while. I could tell Nate was really into me. Just by the way he kept touching me and giving me looks.

I was attracted to him too. But one thing bummed me out—the way he kept getting serious, asking me questions about my life back home and what it was like being a Fear.

What was his *problem*, anyway?

Finally, he told me about some weird things that had happened to him in October. The stories were totally bizarre. He said one night at the bar, cockroaches started pouring out of his mouth. And then one day in school, both of his ears started spurting blood for no reason at all.

Yikes.

He said everyone believed Candy Shutt was using Angelica Fear's amulet to cast spells on him. But it turned out not to be true.

Was someone else doing these things to Nate?

Was there someone out there who knew how to put curses on people? Someone who really wanted to hurt Nate and his friends?

The whole idea sounded crazy to me.

"You're a Fear, right?" Nate said, squeezing my arm. "Do you know spells and sorcery and stuff? Do you know how to do things to people you hate?"

I just stared at him. My head was kinda buzzing from the beers I'd drunk. And my eyes weren't totally focusing.

But I could think straight enough to know that I didn't like his questions.

I shoved my beer bottle in front of him. "Drink some more," I snapped. "Maybe you'll make more sense."

"No. Really—," he started.

"Nate, I don't know what you're talking about," I told him. "How would I know anything about that? Just because I'm a Fear doesn't mean I'm interested in—"

"Sorry. Sorry," he said. He leaned over and kissed me on the cheek. "Sorry. Really. Sorry. Umm, did I say I was sorry?"

Shark laughed. "Kiss her again, Nate."

I glanced up—and saw Ada staring at us from the middle of the room.

Did she see Nate kiss me?

Yes. It was easy to tell from the angry scowl on her face.

"Hey, Ada—," Nate started. "Scoot over, Shark. Make room—"

But before anyone could move, Ada grabbed Nate by the arm and pulled him from the booth. He had a goofy, confused look on his face. He half-stumbled, half-shuffled after her. I saw her pin him to the wall next to the bathrooms.

"Ada, want a beer?" Shark shouted. He grinned at me. The whole thing was a joke to him.

But I had this heavy feeling in the pit of my stomach. And my head started to buzz even louder.

The three guys at my table all started talking at once. But they didn't drown out Ada.

I could hear her getting into Nate's face. I couldn't hear her words because she was speaking in a loud whisper. But you didn't have to be a genius to figure out what she was saying.

And then I heard these words from Nate: "I'm just trying to be nice to her. It's tough being the new kid."

Ow. That hurt.

And then I heard Ada's furious reply: "Don't be *too* nice to her. Hear me?"

Whoa.

After that, it got ugly. The two of them started shouting at each other. Ada no longer cared if I heard or not.

I jumped to my feet when I heard her scream, "She's trying to take my boyfriend *and* my scholarship!"

I saw the smile fade from Shark's face. He lurched over to break it up.

But I didn't care. I'd heard enough. No way I was going to sit there and pretend it wasn't all about me.

I turned and ran. Ran down the long bar, pushed open the front door, and darted out into the cold, clear night.

Breathing hard. My heart pounding. I watched my breath puff up in front of me. And I cried out loud to the empty street, "What am I going to do about Ada?"

16

Saturday night a fog settled over Fear Lake, giving it an eerie, dreamlike feel. Pale rays of moonlight poked through the billowing fog, making dappled spots over the ice.

It was my turn to keep an eye on Jamie's little brother Danny for a few hours. So the skating party was underway by the time I arrived.

Some kids had set up tents at the edge of the frozen lake. They were serving hot chocolate from big, silver urns, and I saw cans of soda and beer stacked in another tent. A small bonfire sent up orange and yellow flames into the foggy sky.

A guy I recognized from school stood behind two turntables and a pair of loudspeakers. He must have had a portable generator. His music blasted out over the voices of kids skating, clustered in couples and groups, and huddled near the tents.

It hadn't snowed yet this fall, but the lake appeared frozen solid, and the ground along the shore was crunchy and hard. Chunks of frost crinkled under my boots.

I wore two sweaters under my parka, a long, striped scarf around my neck, and a wool ski cap pulled down over my ears, but I still shivered from the frigid, damp air.

"Hey, Dana—yo!"

I turned and saw Jamie standing with Lewis at the edge of the ice. I hurried over to them.

I had Jamie's skates slung over my shoulder. Jamie couldn't use them because her hip and leg weren't recovered enough to skate.

"Nate was looking for you," Lewis said. He pointed with his soda can to a group of kids huddled under a tree, singing along at the top of their voices with the DJ's cranked-up music.

I recognized Nate. He motioned for me to join him.

Jamie squinted at me. "You're here with Nate?"

I just waved my hand. I didn't answer. I

turned and half-ran, half-slid over to Nate and his friends. As I drew closer, I recognized Shark and Nikki, and Aaron and Galen. They all waved and called out to me.

I slid right into Nate. Laughing, he caught me around the waist. He held on to me for a little while, which I didn't mind at all.

"Are we having fun yet?" Shark asked.

The fog swirled around us. Circles of yellow moonlight slid over the frozen lake. It was hard to see where the shore ended and the lake began.

"Dana, want a beer?" Nate reached for a six-pack beside him on the ground.

"No thanks," I said. I swung Jamie's skates off my shoulder. "You just going to stand here drinking beer? I thought we were going to skate."

"Some of us came for the beer," Shark said.

Nikki gave him a hard shove. "You promised we'd skate. You told me you're a killer skater. You said you made the state hockey finals last year."

Aaron and Galen tossed back their heads and laughed.

"I'm totally shocked," Nate said. "Shark *never* lied before!"

More laughter.

"Maybe I exaggerated about my skating a little," Shark confessed.

Nikki glared at him. "Tell the truth. Have you ever been on ice skates?"

Shark hesitated. He grinned at Nikki. "Do they go on your feet, or what?"

Nikki gave him another shove.

"Hey, I can still skate better than Nate," Shark told her.

"No way," Nate said. "Want to make a bet on it?"

"Can't we just skate for fun and party tonight without any bets?" I asked, leaning against Nate.

"What do you want to bet?" Shark asked Nate, ignoring me. "How about the rest of that beer?"

He grabbed the can from Nate's hand, tilted it to his mouth, and drained it. "See? I won the bet already!"

Nikki shook her head at Shark. "How not funny are you?"

He kissed her. "You love it," he said.

"Well, I'm putting on my skates," I told Nate. "Are you coming with me?"

He nodded.

I pulled him to a bench at the edge of the lake. We strapped on our skates, watching kids already on the ice. They appeared to float through the swirls of fog.

Couples skated together in graceful circles. One guy took a running jump, dove forward, and went sliding headfirst at full speed over the ice into a group of girls.

They scattered, squealing and laughing.

"That's Dan Nickerson," Nate told me. "He does that every year."

"Cute," I said.

Nate pulled me to my feet, and we skated out onto the lake. We made wide circles at first, skating slowly. I hadn't been on ice skates in years, but it quickly came back to me.

Nate was a pretty good skater. But he kept grabbing my hand to steady his balance. We were far out on the lake. At least, it seemed far out. Squinting through the fog, I could barely see the tents and the kids on the shore.

Nate grabbed my gloved hand and held on. We slowed to a stop. He pulled me close and kissed me. I kissed him back. I let him know I was enjoying it.

How long did we kiss?

I don't know. I pulled away from him when I heard someone shouting my name. Breathless, I turned and saw Jamie running across the ice toward us.

She was limping and sliding, waving her arms to keep her balance. "Dana? Is that you?" she called.

I broke away from Nate and took a few sliding steps toward her. "Jamie, what's wrong?"

"Ada," she gasped, struggling to catch her breath. She bent over, pressing her hands on her knees.

"What about Ada?" Nate asked.

"She's here," Jamie said, pointing to the shore. "She's looking for you, Dana. She found out you're here with Nate."

I squinted at her. "Excuse me?"

"I mean, she's out of control. So mad!" Jamie said. "I just wanted to warn you."

"Oh, wow," I muttered.

Jamie limped away, shaking her head.

I saw a blur of movement to her left. Through the curtain of fog, I recognized Ada, bent low, skating fast.

Nate shook his head angrily. "Forget it," he said. "I don't need this."

"But, wait—," I protested. "Don't leave me here." My heart started to pound in my chest.

He skated off, head down, taking long strides.

"That's not fair!" I shouted.

Ada came roaring toward me. She wore layers of sweaters over tight jeans. Her long scarf flew behind her like a flag.

"Ada—stop!" I cried.

"You can't have him!" she shouted. "You can't come here and ruin my life!"

Sobbing, she bumped me hard. I toppled backward. But she grabbed me and held me up.

"Ada—please!"

She grabbed my shoulders and started to shake me.

"Let go! Let go!" I screamed, struggling to squirm away.

But she lowered her gloved hands and curled them around my throat. "You can't! You can't!" she uttered.

"Ada—*stop*!" I pleaded as her fingers tightened. I suddenly felt dizzy. I couldn't breathe.

"Stop! You're *choking* me!"

17

I opened my eyes. I blinked a few times, trying to focus.

I felt so dizzy. My ears rang.

Had I blacked out or something?

I took a deep breath and gazed around. I was sitting on the ice, with my legs spread. My throat ached. My heart pounded hard.

I shut my eyes again. Why did I feel so wiped? So weak, I couldn't raise my arms?

When I opened my eyes again, I could see kids skating toward me, their faces hidden in the thickening fog. I heard shouts, but I couldn't understand the words.

Confused, I tried to pull myself up. But I sank back onto the ice, my head spinning.

What *happened* to me?

Jamie's voice broke through the ringing in

my ears. I felt her gloved hand on my shoulder. I turned and gazed up into her worried face.

"Dana, we heard screams. Where's Ada?"

Huh? Ada?

Jamie turned away from me. Her mouth dropped open, and she squeezed my shoulder so hard, I gasped.

I turned to see what she was staring at. And uttered a sharp cry.

Ada?

Yes. Stretched out on her back on the ice.

Ada . . . Ada in a dark pool of blood.

Ada with an ice skate . . . the blade . . . the blade . . . driven into her head. Standing straight up. Poking out from between her open, glassy eyes.

Without realizing it, I jumped to my feet.

I saw Jamie's accusing stare.

I raised my gloved hands to the sides of my face and I started to scream: "I didn't do it! I didn't do it! I didn't do it . . . !"

PART THREE

18

I've had some hard times lately, with my mom dying and my dad deciding he didn't want me to live with him. And some other painful stuff.

But the next three days were a total nightmare, the worst days of my life.

The Shadyside police showed up about ten minutes after we saw Ada's body. You can imagine the screams of horror and crying and wailing that went on when the other kids all came skating out to take a look at her. And the cold, accusing stares I got.

Every kid there thought I was a murderer.

Including Nate and Jamie, I'm sure.

At least, Jamie stood by me. I don't remember seeing Nate. He simply disappeared.

Anyway, the police took me to their precinct

station in the Old Village. They called Jamie's parents. Her dad is a lawyer, thank goodness.

We all sat around a beat-up, metal table in a tiny, gray room. Everyone grim and yellow-faced under harsh fluorescent ceiling lights.

Jamie's mother kept her eyes down. She wouldn't look at me. Mr. Richards squeezed my hand and whispered that I didn't have to answer any questions I didn't want to.

"I-I'll answer what I can," I stammered.

Two police officers—a man and a woman—questioned me for hours. I told them everything I could.

The last thing I remembered was Ada leaping on me and choking me. I told them I remembered the feeling of her wool gloves, scratchy on my neck. How she tightened her fingers around my throat. How she cut off my windpipe.

I couldn't breathe.

I pleaded with her to let go.

That's all. Nothing more to tell.

The next thing I knew, I was sitting up on the ice, feeling dazed. My head felt as if it weighed a hundred pounds, and my eyes wouldn't focus.

I must have blacked out because Ada cut off my air. She tried to choke me to death. I tried to get away. I tried to free myself.

But I didn't fight back. And I didn't kill her.

We went over and over the whole thing. I think the two officers wanted to trick me into changing my story. Or they thought maybe I'd break down and confess.

They checked my neck. And yes, there were red bruises at my throat, just as I'd said.

I had tears streaming down my cheeks. I kept drinking cup after cup of water. My hands shook. I clasped them tightly in my lap and stared across the table at the two cops.

I looked straight into their eyes. I wanted to convince them I was telling the truth.

And finally, I raised my trembling hands. "Look at my hands," I said. "Look at my arms. I don't work out or anything. Look how skinny I am. I'm not strong enough to shove a skate blade through someone's skull. No way."

I held my arms up, and they stared at them. Studied them. I think maybe it helped convince them.

"I was being choked to death," I told them.

"I couldn't breathe. I couldn't fight her off. How could I unlace her skate and drive it through her head?"

"I think we're going to end this now," Jamie's dad said. "Are you going to charge Dana?"

The two officers whispered to each other. Then they left the room.

I turned to Jamie's mom. Mrs. Richards had a handkerchief pressed to her face. I couldn't see her expression.

Mr. Richards patted my hand. "I think they believe you," he murmured. "Did you see anyone else around? Do you know of someone else who had a grudge against Ada or might want to see her dead?"

I stared at him. I'd already answered those questions for the police officers. "No. I don't remember anyone," I said again.

He nodded. "Dana, have you had blackouts before?" he asked.

"No one ever tried to strangle me before," I answered.

But I suddenly remembered that strange, woozy feeling I'd had at the top of the stairs at Jamie's party. I felt so weird that night, as if I was blacking out. And the next thing I knew, I was staring down the stairs at Ada, sprawled on the landing on top of all that broken glass.

I didn't mention it to Jamie's dad. But for the first time all night, the question popped quietly into my mind: *Did* I kill Ada?

Did I go into some kind of weird blackout and murder her without even knowing it?

No.

No way.

No. No. No.

The two officers returned to the room, solemn expressions on their faces. I sucked in a deep breath of air. I thought they were going to arrest me.

But instead, they said they were letting me go. For now. They were continuing their investigation. Blah blah.

I didn't hear the rest.

I was so happy they were letting me go home.

Mrs. Richards started to sob. Jamie's dad put his arm around her, trying to comfort her.

Jamie's dad helped me to their car. I felt like a limp noodle. I could barely walk. He was really nice to me, very gentle and soothing.

Mrs. Richards sat in the front seat of the car and didn't say a word the whole way home.

That was three nights ago.

Now, I sat in Nights Bar at one-thirty on a Wednesday morning, staring at the yellow neon Budweiser sign behind the bar.

I shared a table with Jamie and Lewis. They had both been so sweet to me ever since Saturday night. I don't think I could have survived without them.

You can imagine the cold stares I got when I returned to school Monday morning. And at Ada's funeral, I could tell that everyone there was accusing me of her murder.

Yes, I went to Ada's funeral. I know it would have been easier to stay home. But I wanted to show everyone I am innocent. I had just as much right as anyone else to go to that funeral.

As we made our way from the church, Aaron, Whitney, and Galen deliberately pushed past me. And I heard Aaron murmur the word "murderer."

Now, the three of them sat in a booth in the back of the bar, staring at me coldly, leaning across the table, talking softly, probably about me.

I tried to ignore them. But I felt uncomfortable and totally tense being near people who thought I could do something that horrible.

I wanted to run to their booth and scream, "Yes, I'm a Fear. But that doesn't mean I'm a killer."

Of course I didn't do that. Instead, I tried to make small talk with Jamie and Lewis.

And then Nate walked into the bar.

He kissed the bronze plaque of the Fears and then stared right at me.

Had I talked to Nate since the night of the skating party? No.

Did he call me to ask how I was feeling? Did he call to say he believed in me, he knew I wasn't the murderer? No.

Did he say a single word to me in school? Three guesses.

My breath caught in my throat as he slowly began walking toward our table. I'd been feeling so hurt all week. Hurt that Nate was like all the rest.

I tried to understand it from his side. Yes, he'd been going with Ada. Yes, he'd cared about her too.

But I thought he had real feeling for me. Isn't that why he invited me to the skating party?

He nodded his head to Jamie and Lewis. Then he took my arm. His dark eyes locked on mine. "Dana, can I talk to you?"

He pulled me to the bar. "Nate, where've you been?" I asked. I couldn't hide my anger.

He shook his head. "In a daze, I guess." He didn't let go of my arm. "I'm sorry, Dana. I wanted to call you, but—"

"But what?" I demanded.

"I stayed home," he said, avoiding my gaze. "I couldn't think about anything. I know I should have called or something. But I didn't call anyone. I was . . . scared."

I pushed his hand away. "Scared of *me*?"

"No," he said quickly. "No way. Just scared. I mean, look. It's frightening, right? Two girls in our class are dead."

"And . . . you think that I—?"

"No," he said again. "I don't know what to think, Dana. I—just—"

"I didn't even know Candy," I said. "She died before I came to Shadyside."

"I know," he said.

"How can anyone suspect me?" I cried. "I'm a good person. I'd never kill anyone."

Nate finally raised his eyes to mine. "I know," he said again. And then he wrapped his arms around me and pulled me close.

For a moment, pressed against him, I felt safe. I held my face against his and hugged him tightly.

Suddenly, I realized we weren't alone. I turned to find Whitney, Aaron, and Galen standing in front of us, cold glares on their faces.

"Oh." I let out a startled cry and let go of Nate.

"We heard what you were saying," Whitney said. "Well, why don't you tell us this? If you'd never kill anyone, Dana, what about your boyfriend back home? Tell us you didn't kill him, too!"

19

My breath caught in my throat. I felt my heart skip a beat.

"Dustin?" I choked out. "You found out about Dustin?"

Whitney stared at me coldly, challenging me, her hands pressed tightly at her waist. She nodded. "I have a friend at your old school. She told me the whole story."

I sank back against the wall. I struggled to catch my breath. "But . . . no one *knows* the whole story."

"I do," Whitney sneered. "You killed him, too."

"That's a LIE!" I screamed. "It was a horrible accident. That's what the police said—and that's the truth."

Whitney, Aaron, and Galen stared at me,

waiting for me to tell them more. Nate put his arm around my shoulder. "Jamie told us you've had a hard year," he said softly. "I didn't know your boyfriend died."

I fought back the tears, but I could feel them running down my cheeks. "It was an accident," I said. "Dustin and I . . . we were hanging out in my pool. In my backyard. It was a beautiful afternoon. I went in the house to make us some sandwiches."

I kept my eyes on Nate as I told the story. I couldn't stand the cold, accusing expressions of the other three kids.

"I wasn't feeling well that day. I had a big fight with my father that morning. It messed me up, made me feel horrible. I . . . I was finishing the sandwiches. I heard a splash outside. And . . . and . . ."

Nate squeezed me gently. "It's okay," he whispered. "You don't have to go on if—"

I took a deep breath and continued. I wanted Whitney and the two boys to know the truth.

"I carried the sandwiches to the pool. I . . . dropped the tray when I saw Dustin. He—he was floating facedown in the pool. And the water around him—it was pink. The tray broke and the sandwiches scattered around me. And I just stared at the pink water.

"It took me so long to realize what made the water pink. It was Dustin's blood. I started shouting his name. I thought maybe it was a joke. Maybe he was trying to scare me. He liked to do that. But, no. He was . . . dead.

"I just stood there, frozen, and watched his body bob in the pink water. I didn't scream or anything. I just stood there, not moving, not breathing. Not believing it, I guess.

"The police decided Dustin had tried a dive and hit his head on the side. It must have knocked him unconscious. His head was cracked open and he drowned."

I used my sleeve to wipe the tears from my face. My whole body was trembling. Nate held me tightly.

I turned to my three accusers. Their cold expressions hadn't changed.

"Good story," Whitney muttered, rolling her eyes.

"Whitney, that was the worst day of my life!" I cried. "I really loved Dustin. How *dare* you accuse me! How can you be so cruel?"

Whitney let out a furious shout. She grabbed my T-shirt with both hands and jerked me close to her. "How can I be so cruel?" she screamed. "How can I be so cruel?"

"Let go of me," I said, struggling to pull her hands away.

"How can I be so cruel?" she repeated, spitting the words in my face. "You killed my best friend—that's how. I know you did."

She tightened her grip on my shirt and jerked me hard, back and forth. Her face was bright red now, and tears flowed down her cheeks.

"You killed my best friend!" she shrieked. You killed Ada—just to get her boyfriend and her scholarship!"

"No!" I cried. "No! Let go of me!"

Jamie and Lewis pushed between Aaron and Galen. Jamie grabbed Whitney around the waist and tried to pull her off me.

"You killed Ada!" Whitney screamed. "You killed her! You killed her! You're a Fear—and that means you're a killer!"

Wailing and sobbing, Whitney started pounding me with her fists. Covering my face, I tried to squirm away.

I heard Ryland shouting.

Someone pulled Whitney away.

I lowered my hands and saw Galen and Aaron holding her, helping her out of the bar. She was sobbing at the top of her lungs, shaking her fists wildly in front of her.

Trembling, my heart racing, I turned to Jamie. "What am I going to do? She's crazy," I whispered. "She'll convince everyone I'm a murderer. How can I stop her?"

20

Friday night I was hunched over my laptop trying to do some homework when Nate IM'd me:

> *Dana, r u there? Can I come see u?*

I was in a bad mood. I messaged him back:

> *Aren't u afraid to be alone with a murderer?*

He ignored my question and wrote:

> *c u soon.*

I jumped up and hurried to change out of the torn T-shirt and baggy jeans I was wearing. I pulled on a bright pink sweater over straight-legged black pants. Very sexy. I pulled a necklace from my dresser drawer and slid it around my neck.

Then I put on lip gloss and brushed my hair.

I kept thinking about Nate, how he held me in the bar, how he hugged me. How he tried to protect me from Whitney's attack.

But a lot of questions nagged at the back of my mind.

What did Nate really think?

He didn't call me for three days after Ada died. Why not? Because he thought I killed Ada?

If not, who did he think was the murderer?

Jamie was standing by me. When Whitney glared at me in the hall at school, Jamie glared right back at her. Lewis believed in me too.

And I wanted Nate to trust me. I really did. I needed someone to rely on, and I hoped that someone was Nate.

The doorbell rang. Jamie and Lewis were at a movie. Danny was staying with a friend. Jamie's parents were out too. I was the only one home.

I ran down the stairs and pulled open the front door.

Nate had a smile on his face. But when he saw me, his eyes went wide and his mouth dropped open.

I realized he was staring at my chest. "Nate? What's wrong?" I asked.

"That pendant," he said, pointing. "Where did you get it?"

My hand went to the necklace. "I made it," I said. "Why? What's wrong with it?"

He didn't answer. He grabbed it gently and smoothed his hand over it. The pendant was made of silver wire with blue glass cut to look like jewels.

"It's not old?" he asked finally. He let go of it and took a step back.

"No. I told you. I made it," I said.

It was a cold, blustery kind of night, black storm clouds low in the sky. Nate stood there with his denim jacket open, a black T-shirt underneath. "Aren't you cold?" I said.

I stepped aside and motioned for Nate to come into the house. I closed the door behind him. He was still studying the pendant.

"It just looks old," I said. "I copied the design from old photos of Angelica Fear."

He swallowed. "You did? You have photos of Angelica Fear?"

I nodded. "Well, yes. I told you I've studied the history of the Fears. It *is* my family, after all." I tugged his arm. "Want to see the photos of her?"

"For sure," he said.

I led him up to my room in the attic. He looked around, ducking his head under the slanting ceiling. "Cozy," he said. He grabbed my arms and tried to pull me on top of him on the bed.

"Hey, I thought you wanted to see old photos," I said.

He kissed me. We kissed for a while. I held the sides of his face, held him there, needing him, needing someone to care about me.

Then, breathless, I pulled away and dropped down to my file drawer. He sat on the bed and watched me as I searched for the Angelica Fear photos.

"Here." I handed both of them to him. "The date on the back says eighteen ninety-five. They're pretty faded. I had to tape that one back together. It kinda crumbled."

He studied the first photo for a long time, then moved to the second one. "That's the amulet," he murmured.

"Do you know about it?" I asked.

He didn't answer. Just stared from one photo to the other.

"Angelica Fear was obsessed with immortality," I said. "I read a lot about her. She was one of the most interesting Fears—and one of the most evil. She was into all kinds of witch-craft and sorcery. She did a lot of experiments, trying to bring dead people back to life. She said she would live forever. She told people she had found the secret."

Nate finally put down the photos. He gazed at me. I didn't know if he'd heard a word I said. "Why did you copy her amulet?" he asked.

I shrugged. "I just thought it was kinda cool. You know. Mysterious looking. I was really into jewelry-making for a while. Jamie isn't the only artistic one in the family."

He turned back to the amulet. "Did Angelica wear it because it had magical pow-ers? Was that her secret for living forever?"

I shrugged. "Beats me. Maybe she thought it had powers. I didn't read about that any-where."

I turned the amulet over in my hand. "Do you believe in that supernatural stuff, Nate?"

He snickered. A strange smile spread over his face. "I may know more about the amulet than you do, Dana," he said.

I stared at him. "Excuse me? What are you talking about?"

He let out a sigh and leaned back on my bed. "Can I trust you? I've been dying to tell this to someone."

"Of course you can," I said. I dropped down beside him on the bed and took his hand. "What's wrong, Nate? What is it?"

"This is a secret," he said, lowering his voice. "I know how Candy died. I mean, I was there. It was because of this amulet."

I grabbed the amulet. "Not *this* one."

"No," he said. "Another copy of it. A plastic copy of it. Candy wore it all the time. Shark and I—we didn't know it was plastic. We thought it was really Angelica Fear's amulet. And we thought Candy was using it to put a curse on us."

I squeezed his hand. "A curse? You mean the cockroaches? The blood spurting from your ears?"

He nodded. "There's more. One day my car drove into the river with four of us inside it. We almost drowned."

I shook my head. "Wow. And you thought Candy . . ."

"Yes. We thought Candy was doing it. You've got to swear not to tell anyone, Dana. I've had this secret inside me for weeks. Late one night, Shark, Nikki, and I sneaked into Candy's house. We knew she was all alone. We wanted to steal the amulet. But . . ."

"But what happened?" I asked.

"We took it from her room. But she woke up. She tried to grab it back. And . . . and she fell down the stairs. She broke her neck. She was dead. We knew she was dead. And we just ran. And then . . . then we found out her amulet was a fake. Just like yours."

I stared at him and held on to his hand. I could see the horror on his face. I hoped it had helped him to tell the story to someone.

"We never told anyone we were there that night when Candy died," he said. "But here's the weird part. Later, I went to bed—and I found a pig's head in my bed. A bloody pig's head under my covers."

I gasped. "But—how? What does that mean?"

He lowered his voice to a whisper. "It means there's something evil out there. I don't know why. I can just feel it, Dana."

He grabbed me and held on to me. "I know you didn't kill Ada. But someone did. And . . . and Candy didn't just fall. She went *flying*. It wasn't natural. It was like an invisible force pushed her."

"An invisible force?" I said, my voice trembling. "Evil? You really believe that?"

He nodded.

I hugged him and held him tightly. He was so tense, I could almost feel the fear in his body.

"Something evil out there . . ." As I pressed my cheek against his, the words repeated in my mind.

Impossible, I thought. Impossible.

But, Monday afternoon, I started to agree with him.

21

Four folding chairs were lined up in a row in front of the curtain on the auditorium stage. I stared at the four chairs as I walked down the aisle, and my throat tightened.

I can't sing today, I thought. I'm too nervous.

Get it together, Dana, I scolded myself. I had no choice. I had to sing. This afternoon was the first round in the singing competition for the Collingsworth Prize.

I saw ten or twelve kids hunched in seats near the stage. Jamie waved to me. She and Lewis had come to cheer me on.

At the side, Ms. Watson sat with three other teachers. They all had clipboards in their laps. They were the judges. I waved to Ms. Watson, and she smiled back.

My throat felt even tighter. I struggled to swallow. My mouth suddenly felt as if it were filled with sand.

How can I do this?

I felt a hand tap me on the shoulder. Startled, I jumped.

Nate grinned at me. "Sorry. A little tense?"

"You got that right," I said. "Are you staying for the contest?"

He nodded. "I'm going to send you good vibes. Who else is singing? Whitney, right?"

The sound of her name sent a shiver down my back. "Yeah, Whitney," I said. "And Sharona and Yuri."

Nate's eyes went wide. "Yuri? He's a math nerd. I didn't know he could sing."

"Jamie says Yuri can do everything," I replied.

Nate squeezed my shoulder. "Don't worry about him. You're gonna win this thing. It's a piece of cake. I know it."

"I *need* to win it," I said. "If I don't, my life is garbage." I realized I was squeezing the amulet, almost tugging it off its chain.

Nate kissed me on the cheek. "Go get 'em."

I glanced up to the stage. Whitney had already taken her seat at the end of the row of folding chairs. She looked very prim in a loose, white top and a knee-length gray skirt. She was straightening her long, blond hair with one hand.

When she saw me, her smile faded. Her face went hard. She glared at me and mouthed a word.

I recognized it: MURDERER.

"Whitney hates me so much," I whispered to Nate. "Check out that look on her face."

Nate raised his eyes to the stage. "Cold," he murmured.

"Jamie tried to reason with her," I said, holding on to his arm. But Whitney wouldn't listen." I sighed. "Jamie and Whitney were good friends—before I showed up."

Nate gripped my shoulders. "Hey, forget all that," he said. "Don't think about Whitney. Just get up there and sing."

I nodded. "You're right. Thanks, Nate."

I followed Yuri and Sharona onto the stage. I took the chair at the far end, as far away from Whitney as I could get.

I hoped I didn't have to sing first. I needed

time to get my head together. But wouldn't you know it? Ms. Watson motioned for me to step to the microphone.

I handed her my music and tried to clear my throat, taking deep breaths as she walked to the piano. I knew Whitney was sending me hate vibes. I looked straight out at the kids in the audience.

I sang "Mister Snow," from the Broadway musical *Carousel*. I probably should have done something classical. But I knew this was my best song.

I did okay. Not my best performance. My voice was a little thin in the beginning. I could hear it, but I hoped maybe the judges didn't notice.

When I finished, Jamie, Nate, and Lewis went wild, cheering and shouting. The other kids clapped politely.

As I took my seat, I glanced at the judges. They were scribbling furiously on their clip-boards. One of them had a smile on her face. The other two had blank expressions.

I turned and saw Whitney striding over to Ms. Watson at the piano. She handed her some sheet music, then stepped up to the microphone, tugging her top down over her skirt.

I shut my eyes. I suddenly felt kinda strange. Dizzy. A little faint.

Just tension, I told myself.

Whitney announced that she was singing a number by Dvořák. She cleared her throat noisily. Ms. Watson started to play.

Whitney opened her mouth to sing—but stopped.

She sneezed.

Ms. Watson stopped playing. She turned to Whitney. "Ready now?"

Whitney raised a hand, signaling for Ms. Watson to wait. She sneezed again. Then again. Loud, violent sneezes.

Whitney's eyes bulged. "Aaaack!" Whitney let out a cry. She reached up to her nose and started to pull something out. Something slender and white.

At first, I thought it was a Kleenex or a handkerchief. But then I realized Whitney had pulled a *feather* from her nose.

Some kids giggled. I heard a few gasps.

Whitney held the feather in two fingers, staring at it in bewilderment.

"Whitney, are you okay?" Ms. Watson called from the piano.

Whitney didn't reply. She sneezed again. "Ohhhhh." A low groan escaped her throat. Slowly, very slowly, she pulled another long, white feather from her nose.

This time, no one laughed. The auditorium grew very quiet.

"Aaaack. Oh, help!"

Whitney tugged another long feather from her nose. As soon as it was in her hand, another feather poked out. She pulled it out quickly, and another feather appeared.

"NOOOOOOOO!" Whitney opened her mouth in a scream of horror.

Still feeling dizzy and faint, I gripped my pendant and watched the slender, white feathers float to the stage floor at her feet.

Feather after feather slid out. And then the auditorium erupted in screams as the feathers came out bright red. Blood started to flow from her nose.

Whitney sneezed hard. Again. Again.

She screamed and pulled out another blood-soaked feather.

"Help me! Somebody—HELP me!"

The feathers piled at her feet, and the glistening, red blood poured onto the feathers.

The blood ran down the front of her white blouse. Another dripping, red feather slid from her nose.

Whitney spun around and shook a finger at me. "DANA is doing this!" she shrieked. "She's using her Fear powers! She's doing this to me!"

Lots of gasps and startled cries in the audience. The three judges were on their feet, their faces tight with horror.

Whitney covered her face, but the blood continued to flow, pouring from her nose, puddling at her already blood-soaked shoes.

22

"Dana, my mom's very worried about you," Jamie said, poking her head into my room. "You didn't come down to dinner."

I was sprawled on my back in bed, reading an old copy of *People* magazine. I dropped the magazine to my side. "I'm just not hungry," I said. "Tell her I'll grab something later."

Jamie crossed the room, stepping over the dirty clothing I'd tossed in a pile. She sat down on the edge of the bed. "You've been moping around for three days. You've been acting so weird. Ever since . . ."

I pulled myself up to a sitting position. I felt my stomach churning. Every muscle in my body was tense and knotted. "Of *course* I've been acting weird. I'm like a freak at school!" I cried.

Jamie narrowed her eyes at me. I could see she was surprised by my outburst.

"Ever since the thing with Whitney," I continued, unable to keep my voice steady. "No one is talking to me, Jamie. I'm a total outcast. I say hi to people, and they cut me dead. They don't even look at me."

"But, Dana—," Jamie started.

"Everyone thinks I made the feathers come out of Whitney's nose. Because I'm a Fear, everyone thinks I used magic to keep Whitney from singing. But that's CRAZY!"

I was screaming now, my voice so high that even dogs couldn't hear it. Jamie tried to take my hand, but I jerked it away.

"I don't know any magic!" I cried. "And I wouldn't do that to Whitney. My name is Fear, but I'm not evil. I don't know any tricks at all. How could I make feathers appear in Whitney's nose? No way! How can anyone even *think* I could do it?"

Jamie stood up. She bit her bottom lip, studying me.

I had tears in my eyes. Angry tears. I wiped them away before they could slide down my cheeks.

"Can I give you one piece of advice?" Jamie asked, speaking softly.

I nodded.

"Don't wear that amulet to school. I know you made it and everything. But a lot of kids are afraid of it."

"Huh? Okay," I said. I ripped it off my neck and tossed it in the trash.

I sneaked out of the house a little after one in the morning and made my way to Nights Bar on Fear Street.

I wasn't going to go. I didn't want more kids staring at me—those cold, accusing stares. I knew I couldn't take it much longer.

I'd gone to bed early. I wrapped myself up in a tiny ball, hugging my pillow like a teddy bear, and tried to sleep.

But Nate called on my cell and begged me to come to the bar. He said he really wanted to talk to me.

So here I was. In a worn sweater and an old pair of jeans, torn at the knees. Did I stop to brush my hair? I couldn't even remember.

A cool, clear night. Lots of stars twinkling

in the sky. No one else around, of course. The town asleep, except for us.

I waved to Ryland O'Connor and purposely didn't kiss the bronze plaque of Simon and Angelica Fear. Then Nate pulled me to a booth at the back wall. The bar was crowded with kids. But they were a blur to me. I kept my eyes straight ahead. I didn't care who was there.

I dropped into the booth, and Nate squeezed beside me. He kissed me. He'd been really nice to me ever since that frightening afternoon in the auditorium.

"I . . . didn't want to come out tonight," I said. "But when you called . . ."

He started to unzip my parka. "Are you wearing the amulet?"

"Excuse me?" I moved his hands away. "No. I threw it in the trash."

He squinted at me. "Really? Well, I found out more about it. The real one, I mean."

Ryland came up to the table. Nate ordered a beer. I asked for coffee.

"You did research on it?" I asked.

"Yeah. On the Net," he said. "I found some interesting Web sites."

I pulled off my parka and stuffed it on the other side of the booth. Then I snuggled next to Nate. "What did you learn about the amulet? That it makes feathers fly out of people's noses?"

He shook his head. "Forget about feathers, Dana. Angelica Fear was convinced she could use the amulet to come back from the grave. And—"

"We already know that," I interrupted.

"She believed she could come back from the grave *and inhabit a living person's body,*" Nate said.

I stared at him. "So?"

"Don't you see?" Nate slapped the table-top. "Who else could be doing all these horrible things? It can't be any of us. We're all just trying to slog through high school, right? We're not murderers or sorcerers. We just want to get through senior year and party a little and have some fun."

"I guess . . . ," I said. I didn't really understand where he was going with this.

"So, I've been thinking," Nate continued. "Thinking a lot. I mean, they tore down the old Fear Mansion last year, right? It was on this spot where we're sitting. And they tore down all the other Fear Street houses to put up the shopping center."

"Yeah. Right," I said.

"Well, what if Angelica Fear was buried under the mansion or something?" Nate asked, eyes wide with excitement. "What if her grave was disturbed when they dug up the old place? What if a lot of graves were disturbed, and the ghosts of Fear Street all escaped from them?"

"Nate, please—," I started.

He squeezed my wrist. "Dana, listen. What if Angelica really *did* know how to come back to life? What if she came back to life last year with all her evil tricks and is living inside someone's body. Someone we know!"

"STOP!" I screamed. "I mean it, Nate. Stop! Don't you realize how crazy that sounds?"

His face fell. He looked hurt. "Of course it sounds crazy," he said. "But look at all the crazy things that have been happening. How do you explain—?"

"You've been hanging out with my cousin Jamie too long," I said. "Jamie believes in all that supernatural stuff."

Nate opened his mouth to say something,

but he never got it out. Shark appeared at the table, with Nikki close behind him.

Shark had a black leather jacket open over a black T-shirt, collar up, over black denims. He had a black wool ski cap pulled down over his hair. Nikki's white-blond hair hung wildly about her face. She wore a pale green parka, and brown corduroy pants tucked into furry Ugg boots.

Shark grabbed Nate's shoulder. "Yo, dude. What's up?"

"I'm talking about evil ghosts," Nate said. "Doing evil things to our friends."

"Shut *up*! Are you freaked about Whitney?" Nikki asked. "Shark told me about it, and—"

"Do we have to talk about that stuff?" Shark asked. "Hey, we used to sneak out late at night for *fun*—remember? We're the Night People. We stay up all night. So why aren't we having fun anymore?"

Nate finished his beer. He slammed the bottle on the tabletop. "Yeah. Let's do it. Shark is right. Come on, Dana. Let's go out and just goof around. Like we used to."

The four of us left the bar and stepped out into the cool, still night. The Fear Street Acres shopping center stood across the street from Nights. The stores were dimly lit, the doors and windows barred and locked.

We walked along the shops, peering into windows, joking about the junk we saw, goofing on one another. Shark overturned a few trash cans, just because he could, I guess.

The noise must have awakened a dark-uniformed security guard, who poked his head around the wall of a building. We quickly darted into a store entrance.

I held my breath, listening for his footsteps. But he didn't come after us.

Shark snickered. "Are we having fun yet?"

I held on to Nate as we made our way out of the shopping center. Clouds rolled over the moon. A cold wind ruffled my hair.

We stopped and kissed. The kiss lasted a long time. We had to run to catch up to Nikki and Shark.

A few minutes later, we found ourselves outside the Fear Street Cemetery. Tangled trees formed a wall along the sidewalk. Behind them, I could see ragged rows of low gravestones poking up at strange angles.

The wind whispered through the trees,

shaking the bare limbs, like in a bad horror movie.

"You're supposed to hold your breath when you pass a graveyard," Shark said.

"What happens if you don't?" Nikki asked.

He grinned at her. "Feathers come out of your nose."

Shark and Nate laughed. Nikki gave Shark a hard shove that sent him staggering into a fat tree trunk.

"I thought we weren't going to talk about that," I said.

I turned to Nate. He had his eyes on a tall tree a few feet ahead of us. "Hey, Nate——?" I called. I reached for him, but he ducked away.

I saw the look of horror spread over his face. "Look OUT!" he screamed. "It's the one-eyed bird!"

I squinted up into the tree. I couldn't see it. "Where?" I cried.

Nate pointed frantically to a tree limb. Then he darted to one side. Off-balance, he fell to the grass. "Look out! It's attacking!" he screamed.

He dropped to his knees and raised his arms to shield his face. "Run! It's attacking! *Run!*"

23

My breath caught in my throat. I heard a fluttering sound.

The flap of wings?

No. Dead leaves blown by the wind.

Shark laughed. He pulled Nate to his feet. "You're joking, right?" he said.

His face knotted with terror, Nate searched the treetops. "The bird—"

"What's your problem?" Shark asked him. "None of us saw any bird. It was probably leaves falling or something."

I took Nate's arm. He was trembling, breathing hard. "I saw it," he insisted. "It came swooping down at me."

"Whoa. Creepy," Nikki said.

Shark grinned. He turned to me. "How many beers did Nate have tonight?"

"No. I saw it," Nate repeated. "I saw the blackbird." He shook his head. "What's *happening* to me?"

Nate said to meet him in the gym after school on Monday. I wasn't feeling great. I had a throbbing headache, and I'd been feeling dizzy and kinda weak again.

Just nerves, I hoped.

The thud of a basketball on the gym floor made my head pound. Some kids were having a relaxed game of basketball. I recognized Nate and Yuri and Shark and some girls from my class.

And then I saw Whitney. The others were laughing and kidding around. But she had this intense expression on her face. I watched her dribble up to Shark, fake him out, and go in to score with a driving layup.

Whitney is on the varsity girls' team, I remembered.

I turned to leave, but Nate came running over. "Hey, Dana. How's it going? Go get some sneakers on. Join us."

"I don't think so," I said. "I'm not feeling great, and—"

No way I'd join a game with Whitney on the court.

What was Nate thinking?

"Hey, come on—get in the game!" Shark shouted, waving to me. "We're going to play shirts and skins. The girls are going to be the skins!"

Some kids actually laughed at that.

"I'm feeling kinda weird," I told Nate. "I'll wait for you over there." I pointed to the bleachers.

I took a seat in the second row. I rubbed my forehead with my fingers, trying to rub the ache away. I had my eyes closed. I listened to the *thud thud thud* of the ball and the scrape of sneakers over the floor.

I heard a shout and opened my eyes—in time for the ball to smash me in the chest.

"Hey—" I uttered a shocked cry. Pain shot through my body.

"Oh. Sorry," Whitney said in this fake tone. "It got away from me."

I knew she deliberately heaved it at me. I wanted to jump up and strangle her!

"I'm okay," I said.

Shark picked up the ball and tossed it downcourt to Yuri. The game started up again.

Whitney was the best player on the floor. She seemed to be beating everyone single-handedly.

After a while, I heard someone shouting my name. I turned to the gym doors and saw Jamie waving at me. "I'm going to my pottery class," she shouted. "See you later!"

I waved to her. When I turned back, the game was breaking up. "Dana—I'll be right out," Nate called. He followed Shark and Yuri to the locker room to get changed.

The girls were trotting off the court too. "Whitney, are you coming?" one of them called.

"In a few minutes," Whitney shouted back. "I keep messing up these jump shots."

Whitney and I were alone in the gym now. I leaned back against the bleacher and watched her do jump shot after jump shot. She never looked my way. She was totally intent on getting her jump shots right.

I suddenly felt a wave of nausea roll down my body. I blinked, feeling dizzy. I felt my heart jump in my chest.

Why do I feel so weird? I wondered.

I shut my eyes. I rested my head in my hands, waiting for the strange feeling to pass by.

Everything went gray. Like a thick fog.

Did I pass out? I don't know.

The next thing I knew, Nate was shaking me hard by the shoulders. "Dana? Dana?" He kept repeating my name in a high, tense voice.

I opened my eyes. I shook my head, trying to clear it.

"Nate? What's wrong?"

He turned. It took a while for my eyes to focus. When they finally did, I saw a girl. Lying on her back on the gym floor, arms and legs outstretched.

"Ohh." I uttered a low moan. I recognized Whitney's bright red sneakers.

And then I saw the blood. A bright red puddle spreading over the floor at her shoulders. Her shoulders . . . her neck . . .

I jumped to my feet. My legs trembled. My breath caught in my throat. "Nate—?" I gasped.

I stared at the headless body on the floor. And then I raised my eyes and saw the head— blond hair falling over her face . . . I saw the head up in the basket.

Whitney's head staring blankly down at me from the bloodstained net.

PART FOUR

24

I had no one I could talk to after that. Even Nate sounded different when I talked to him.

I called his cell late Wednesday night. I didn't want to go to Nights, but I couldn't bear to be alone, either. "I just need to talk," I told Nate.

"You kinda woke me up," he said.

"I don't care," I snapped. I was in bed with the blankets pulled up over my head. But I still didn't feel safe. "You have no idea what my life has been like," I said.

I heard Nate yawn. "Listen, Dana—"

"Thank God Jamie's dad is a lawyer," I said. "He's been so wonderful. He sat in while the police questioned me. He took care of everything."

"Great," Nate said sleepily. "That was lucky."

"I called my own dad," I continued. "I told him I was in major trouble. Know what he said? He said he was on a big business trip and couldn't make it. Do you believe that?"

"Weird," Nate replied.

What was with the one-word answers? Was he deliberately acting cold to me?

He couldn't believe I killed Whitney—*could* he?

I didn't care. I had to talk to someone. I had to let it all out.

"The police were tough," I continued, squeezing my cell against my ear. "They think they see a pattern. So far, two girls competing for the Collingsworth Prize have been killed: Ada and Whitney. They know how desperate I am to win that prize. So . . . I have a motive. A motive for killing those two."

"Oh, wow," Nate murmured.

"I don't think they believed me about my blackouts. About how dizzy and faint I felt. How I kinda passed out and everything went gray. They're checking with my doctor back home. But it *never* happened to me back home!"

I took a deep breath. My heart was hammering in my chest. "Sure, the prize means a lot to me," I told Nate. "But I'm not a killer. And I'll tell you one thing the police never mentioned."

"What's that?" Nate asked.

"If someone is killing all the Collingsworth contestants, I could be next. Don't you see? I could be the next victim!"

"Don't think like that," Nate said. "You'll be okay."

I was shivering under the blankets. Nate sounded so cold and insincere. I suddenly felt terrified—and totally alone.

"I've got to catch some sleep," he said, yawning.

"Bye," I said, and clicked off the phone.

I stifled a sob. Was he just tired, or was he like all the others? They all believed I killed those girls.

Was it possible?

Could I have murdered them while I was in that gray fog? Could I be guilty and have no memory of what I'd done?

No. No way. I wouldn't let myself think that way. Not for a moment.

I dropped my cell phone to the floor. Nate's cold, uninterested voice lingered in my ears. I sat up and shoved the blankets away.

I knew I couldn't sleep. I had to talk to someone, someone who believed in me.

Jamie.

When I came home from the police station Monday night, she threw her arms around me and hugged me. I could feel the hot tears on her cheeks.

"I know you didn't do it," she whispered. "I know you didn't. I'll stick by you, Dana. No matter what happens next."

Yes, Jamie seemed to be my last remaining friend. I hoped she hadn't sneaked out to Nights. I really needed her tonight.

I climbed out of bed and straightened my nightshirt. I pushed back my hair. Then I tiptoed down the attic stairs and across the hall to Jamie's room.

Was she in there? Her bedroom door was open just a crack. From the hall I could see flickering light inside the room.

I pushed the door open a little more. And realized I was peering into candlelight. Light and shadows danced and darted around the room.

I poked my head in. To my surprise, I saw Jamie down on her knees on the floor. She knelt in a circle of black candles. She had her back to me. I could see her hair, black in the flickering candlelight, flowing wildly behind her head.

What was she doing down there?

I held my breath and listened. She had her head down. She was reciting something, chanting words I didn't recognize. Her voice was soft and low, rising and falling in a strange melody.

I listened, not moving, not breathing.

What language was that?

A chill ran down my back. I grasped the door handle.

Squinting into the orange light, I saw little bowls on the floor. Chanting softly, Jamie bent over them. She lifted a bowl and poured a dark powder into another bowl.

I watched her sift the powder with her fingers. She poured the powder from bowl to bowl, bending low, chanting in that strange, musical language.

I wanted to call out to her. But I didn't dare interrupt.

And then she turned. And I saw her face.

Gripping the door, I stared wide-eyed at her face, flickering in the orange light.

But it wasn't her face.

Older eyes. A turned-up nose. An aged, ragged, half-smile.

Definitely not Jamie's face!

25

I ducked back. I didn't want her to see me.

I'm imagining this, I decided. It's just the darkness, the shadows falling over the orange light.

No. I could see the face clearly. A woman's face—not Jamie's face.

My heart fluttering in my chest, I turned and stumbled to the stairs. I pulled myself up to my room, dove into bed, and tugged the covers to my chin.

Impossible, I thought. Impossible. *Impossible.* I kept repeating the word in my mind.

But the picture of that face—the *other face*—wouldn't go away.

My brain whirred. I struggled to make

sense of what I saw. But I couldn't explain it. I didn't have a clue.

Did she see me? Did Jamie see me watching her from the doorway?

Another shiver rolled down my back. I struggled to catch my breath, to slow my racing heartbeats.

And then I heard a sound. A soft creak. The creak of the attic stairs.

I sucked in a deep breath and held it. And listened.

Yes. Footsteps on the attic stairs. Another creak.

In the dim, gray light from the hall, I saw Jamie creep into my room. Her face was hidden in shadow. I pretended to be asleep but kept my eyes open just a crack, open enough to watch her.

She hesitated in the doorway. Stood perfectly still. Making sure I wasn't awake, I guessed.

Then she made her way to the couch. I had my school clothes there, laid out for tomorrow morning. A skirt, long-sleeved top, tights.

I lifted my head off the pillow to see better.

Jamie carried something in her hand. Squinting hard, I recognized one of the small bowls. I watched her reach into the bowl. She began to sprinkle powder over my clothes. And as her fingers moved back and forth, she chanted softly, murmuring words in that strange language.

What was she chanting? What was she *doing*?

An ancient spell?

I couldn't breathe. I couldn't move.

I watched in icy horror as my cousin emptied the bowl of powder over my clothes. And I listened to her strange, soft song in that raspy, whispered voice.

Not her voice. Not Jamie's voice at all.

Staring in horrified disbelief, I squeezed the edge of the blanket till my hands ached. And when she finally tiptoed from the room, I sat up with one thought in my mind:

I've got to get out of this house!

26

I waited until I was sure Jamie had gone downstairs. Then I crept across the room and clicked my bedroom door shut.

My hand trembled as I grabbed my cell phone off the floor. And pushed in a number. "Dad, it's me," I whispered.

"Huh? Dana? You woke me up. What time is it?"

"Dad, I know it's the middle of the night. But you have to come get me. Now."

"Dana? What? What are you saying?"

"You've got to take me away from here," I pleaded. "There's something *sick* going on. And—"

"Dana, are you high on something? Are you drunk? Why are you calling me so late?"

"Just listen to me, Dad. Please. For once.

Just listen to me. I need you to listen. It's Jamie. She—"

"What about Jamie? Speak up. I can barely hear you."

"I can't speak up. She'll hear me. Dad, I'm frightened. Seriously frightened. Jamie is using some kind of magic. I don't know what she's up to. I saw her sprinkle my clothes with powder. I think she's trying to poison me or something. Dad—"

"Dana, you're talking crazy," he said. "Listen to what you're saying. You're not making sense. Have you been drinking?"

"I know it sounds crazy, but it isn't," I insisted, my voice breaking with emotion. "You've *got* to believe me. She's doing something to me and—"

"Calm down. Just calm down. Take a breath, okay? Get some sleep, Dana. You'll feel a lot better in the morning."

"No. You've *got* to come get me, Dad."

"Look. I'm in Atlanta. I can't just drop everything."

"Dad, please—"

"Tell you what. I'll try to come next weekend. I think I can clear my schedule. But get yourself together. I mean it. You're talking like a crazy person."

"Dad—?"

He hung up.

I didn't sleep all night. I thought about packing up my stuff and running away. But where could I go?

In the morning, I left the skirt and top on the couch. I put on a different outfit, a loose-fitting black turtleneck over green cords. I grabbed my backpack and crept downstairs.

I heard voices in the kitchen. I poked my head through the doorway. Jamie sat at the kitchen table, finishing a bowl of cereal. Her mom stood at the kitchen counter, a white mug of coffee in her hand.

"No breakfast for me," I said. "I'm going right to school."

"No. I'm sorry," Aunt Audra said. When she turned to me, I saw that her eyes were brimming with tears. "I'm sorry, Dana. I can't let you go to school."

My mouth dropped open. "Excuse me?"

Jamie set down her cereal bowl. She glared at me icily.

"I'm taking you to a doctor," Aunt Audra said. "Before she died, I promised your mother I'd take good care of you, Dana. And now I'm going to see that you get the help you need."

"Huh? Help?"

What was she talking about?

"Your father called me early this morning," she said. "He's very worried about you too."

My heart leaped to my throat. My knees started to buckle. I grabbed the door frame to keep myself up.

Jamie's eyes burned into mine. Her jaw was set tight. She spoke through clenched teeth. "Why did you say those horrible things about me to your dad, Dana?"

"Jamie, listen—"

"I've been so nice to you," she said. "Why did you tell him I'm trying to poison you?" Jamie's eyes grew colder. She raised her butter knife in her fist.

"I'm terribly hurt," she said. "You shouldn't have done that, Dana. You really shouldn't have. . . ."

27

With a gasp, I dropped the backpack, spun away, and started for the stairs.

"Don't go far," Aunt Audra called. "I'm calling Dr. Wilbur as soon as his office opens."

I hurtled up to my room and slammed the door behind me. I paced furiously back and forth in the tiny room, trying to decide on a plan.

What should I do?

After a few minutes I heard the front door slam. From my tiny attic window I saw Jamie trotting toward school, backpack bouncing on her back.

I waited till she was out of sight. Then I took a deep breath, trying to force my heart to stop pounding, and sneaked downstairs to her bedroom.

Her nightshirt was tossed over the bed. A pile of jeans littered the floor in front of the closet. The black candles had been removed. I saw spots of black candle wax on the carpet.

I glanced around. Shoved to the other side of the bed, I saw the big spell book. The old book we had used to try to call up Cindy from the grave.

The book was open to two pages of tiny type. I dropped down to the floor and raised the book to my lap.

I squinted at the narrow columns of type, trying to find what Jamie had been chanting last night. It didn't take long. At the top of the right-hand page, I found what I was looking for.

A spell to fog a person's mind.

I ran a trembling finger over the ancient words.

Yes. A spell to make a person feel faint. To make their minds go blank.

Had Jamie been using this spell on me?

A hundred thoughts shot through my mind at once—all of them horrifying. I pieced together an insane story—just crazy enough to be true.

Jamie used the spell on me to make me go faint. Then she murdered those two girls. She made it look as if I was the murderer. And I was left with no excuse, except that I'd blacked out.

Why?

That was the unanswered question. Why kill her own friends? Why try to put the blame on me? Why would Jamie do that?

A big piece of the puzzle was missing. But I was too terrified to stick around and find it.

I slammed the book shut and jumped to my feet. I had to get out of the house. Had to find someone who would believe me, who would help me.

I stepped out into the hall.

"Dana?" I heard Aunt Audra call from downstairs. "I reached Dr. Wilbur. I'm driving you there in half an hour. Why don't you come down and have some breakfast?"

No! No way.

I pulled on my parka and sneaked out the front door. I took off running, down the driveway and then along the sidewalk. I crossed the street and kept running.

Gasping for breath, my chest aching, I

stopped a few blocks later. I realized where I was running. I was running to Nate's house. He was the only one who could help me. He *had* to help me.

I knocked on his front door and waited. No answer. I rang the bell. No one. I peeked into the front window but couldn't see anyone. The garage door was open. The car was gone.

He must be on his way to school, I decided. So I took off once again, running hard, not thinking, unable to think about anything but finding Nate and begging him to help me escape.

A few minutes later I spotted him in the student parking lot behind the high school. He was climbing out of his mother's blue Accord.

"Thank goodness!" I cried breathlessly.

But then I saw that he wasn't alone. Standing between two cars, he was talking to someone.

I moved closer, keeping low, hiding behind the parked cars. And I recognized Jamie. She was shaking her head, wiping away tears.

I knew she was telling him about me.

Nate slid his arm around Jamie's shoulders. I could see he was comforting her. And then I heard him say, "Dana trusts me. Maybe I can trick her or something. You know. Help get her to the mental hospital."

28

Around four o'clock that afternoon, I saw Jamie lift the garage door and disappear into her sculpture studio. The door slid down noisily behind her.

I watched from the side of the garden shed. I'd wandered aimlessly all day, trying to make a plan. Trying to decide what to do, where to go. Trying to make sense of everything.

I'm not crazy.

I told myself that a hundred times. I don't belong in a mental hospital. I didn't imagine the spellbook. And I didn't imagine Jamie sneaking into my room and spreading powder on my clothes.

Because of my dear cousin, everyone thought I was a murderer. And everyone thought I was insane. And Aunt Audra and my father probably planned to lock me away in some kind of hospital.

I realized I had no choice. I had to confront Jamie. I had to force her to tell me the truth. And so I waited in the cold, waited by the side of the shed. Waited till she went into her studio.

And now, I took a deep breath and stepped up to the garage door. I slid it open slowly, as quietly as possible, hoping to surprise her.

A blast of warm air greeted me. Jamie had her back to me. She stood at the open door of a huge, flaming pottery kiln, as big as a furnace. I watched her lean toward the kiln, lowering a piece of pottery into the blazing heat.

I let go of the garage door and took a few steps into the studio. A long, well-lit worktable filled the center of the room. A potter's wheel stood at the far end. I glimpsed shelves of red clay pottery—vases and bowls and heads and—

Whoa.

My eyes stopped at the pedestals in front of the worktable. Slender, stone pedestals holding three sculpted heads.

Heads of girls . . .

"Ohhh." I raised my hands to my mouth to stifle the sound of my shocked cry.

I recognized two of the clay heads: Ada and Whitney. Was the third head Candy?

Did Jamie sculpt all three dead girls? And paint them to look so lifelike?

I looked to the back wall. Jamie was still leaning into the open kiln.

I couldn't take my eyes off the sculpted heads. I moved as if in a daze. Hardly realizing what I was doing, I crept up to the pedestals. I reached out a trembling hand. I touched the sculpture of Ada. Touched her cheek.

And opened my mouth in a wail of horror.

The heads . . . they weren't clay. They weren't sculpted.

These were the real heads of the murdered girls!

29

Jamie spun away from the kiln at the sound of my scream. Her eyes went wide with surprise, then narrowed at me coldly.

She moved quickly to the worktable. She picked up a black remote controller and clicked it twice. Behind me, I heard the garage door sliding shut.

"You're locked in," Jamie said, tossing down the controller and moving toward me. "I see you are admiring my art gallery."

"Jamie . . . I—I . . . *why*?" I stammered.

The eyes of the three dead girls stared at me blankly.

"Pretty heads, aren't they?" Jamie said. "And look, Dana—I have an empty pedestal. Whose head do you think should go on it? Yours, maybe?"

I took a step back. I glanced frantically around the garage. No side door. The window was open, but too small to fit through. No way to escape.

I turned back to my cousin. "What have you *done*?" I cried. "Why are these heads—"

My breath caught in my throat.

As I gaped at her, Jamie's face changed. Her eyes darkened. Her cheeks sagged. Her features transformed until she wasn't Jamie anymore.

I realized I was staring at the face I'd seen late last night in Jamie's room. An older woman's face, with icy black eyes and a cruel, tight-lipped smile.

"Jamie isn't here," she said in a dry whisper. "Don't you recognize me, Dana? Don't you know who I am?"

And in that instant, I did recognize her. I recognized her from the photos in my file.

Angelica Fear.

A chill tightened the back of my neck. I stood staring at her, frozen in horror. "I . . . don't understand," I choked out. "How . . . ? Where is Jamie?"

She shrugged. "A year ago, Jamie fell onto my grave in front of the Fear Mansion. So lucky for me. I always knew I could come back to life. I could be immortal."

I pointed. "You . . . you . . ." My teeth were chattering. I couldn't talk.

"I took her body," she said in her low, hoarse whisper. "I'm alive again after a hundred years!"

She reached under her collar and pulled out a jeweled pendant. The amulet! "I have the real one, Dana," she whispered. "The one that has made me immortal." She waved it in front of my face.

"But . . . you killed these girls!" I finally found my voice. Anger was quickly overtaking my fear. "Why, Angelica? Why are you killing the Collingsworth Prize finalists?"

She let the amulet fall to her throat. Her dark eyes flashed. "Are you making a joke, Cousin Dana? The idiotic prize doesn't mean a thing to me. I plan to kill everyone who looted my home. Everyone who broke into the Fear Mansion last year and found my secret room. They took what is mine—and they will all pay for it with their lives."

She petted Candy Shutt's head, smoothing back her red hair.

"I don't understand," I said. "Why did you make it look like *I* was the murderer?"

"To distract everyone," she replied, still petting Candy's head. "To throw suspicion off Jamie so I could do my work."

She moved quickly, spinning away from the poor dead girl's head, and grabbed me by the shoulders. "Enough talk," she said, scowling at me. "You've outlived your usefulness, Cousin dear. And we can't allow you to tell everyone the truth—can we?"

"Wh-what are you doing?" I demanded.

But I didn't need to ask. I knew what she was doing. She was backing me up to the open kiln.

Her fingers tightened around my arms. She pushed me with incredible strength.

"I have a lot more thieves to deal with," she said. "The Night People. They all stole from me, from my house. They all must die."

"Let me go—please!" I begged. "I didn't steal anything! I wasn't around then! Please—stop!"

Gripping my arms, she gave me a hard shove. Back . . . back . . .

I tried to dig my heels in. But my sneakers slid over the concrete floor.

Back . . . back . . .

Her dark eyes glowed with excitement.

I could feel the heat of the kiln burning my back.

"Please—Angelica, please—"

She gave me one last, powerful shove and sent me toppling backward.

30

A wave of burning heat washed over me. As I fell back, toward the open kiln door, I reached out. Reached out with both hands searching for something to grab on to.

My right hand clasped the amulet. As I fell back, I pulled it off Angelica's throat. It clattered to the floor.

I kicked out with my feet. Squirmed away from the kiln. I hit the floor hard on my elbows and knees. My skin burned. I wondered if my clothes would burst into flame.

I saw Angelica bend down to retrieve the pendant.

My one chance. I knew I had only a few seconds.

I jumped up. Dove forward. And shoved her with all my might.

The amulet flew from her hand as Angelica sailed into the kiln.

A scream of horror like the howl of a wild animal burst from inside the kiln. I covered my ears, but I couldn't drown out the horrifying sound.

It seemed to go on for hours. An endless, shrill scream of pain.

Orange and red flames rose high, shooting out in all directions. And then, behind the flames, I saw thick swirls of green . . . a green cloud, putrid, so sour-smelling that I had to hold my breath. Choking clouds of green gas, puff after puff, until the garage was filled.

My eyes watered. The odor made me retch.

I gasped as Jamie's body staggered out from the flaming kiln. She stumbled forward, collapsed in a smoldering heap on the floor. And didn't move.

Choking, retching, I dropped onto my knees beside her. Was it Jamie now? Or Angelica?

The howl of pain continued inside the kiln. The green gas spewed out from the open door.

Jamie opened her eyes. She blinked up at me. "Dana? What's going on? Where am I?" She squinted at me. "Hey—what are *you* doing in Shadyside?"

"Jamie?" I cried. "I live with you now. I moved here last month. Don't you remember?"

She sat up. "You live here? Why don't I remember that?"

She doesn't remember anything, I realized. But she seems okay.

From inside the kiln, the screaming came to an abrupt stop. The putrid, green gas slowly faded away.

I've killed her, I thought joyfully. I've destroyed Angelica Fear. She was consumed in the fire.

And then I saw the amulet. Its blue jewels gleamed up at me from the floor. The *real* amulet. Angelica's secret to immortality. The amulet with all its evil magic.

What should I do with it?

I didn't have to think for long. I decided to grab it and toss it into the kiln after Angelica. Let it burn up with her and be gone forever.

I picked the pendant up from the floor and

swung it in the air by the chain. And as I started to swing it into the open kiln door, I heard a fluttering sound at the garage window and saw movement behind me. A darting black shadow.

"Look out!" Jamie cried.

I turned in time to see a huge blackbird come swooping at me. Screeching, it raised its talons.

As it dove toward me, it turned its head, and I saw its missing eye. A dark socket on one side.

I let out a cry as the enormous bird grabbed the amulet from my hand. Grasped it in one gnarled talon. With another screech, it turned in midair. And flapping its wide, papery wings, it swooped out through the open garage window, carrying the amulet with it.

Stunned, I stayed there on my knees on the garage floor. Jamie climbed slowly to her feet. I could see the confusion in her eyes as she grabbed my hands and pulled me up.

"Dana—I don't understand," she started. But then she saw where I was staring, and she stopped.

I was staring at the three heads on the

pedestals, the heads of the murdered girls. Their eyelids began to blink. Their mouths opened. They licked their dry, shriveled lips with purple-black tongues.

And then, as I grabbed Jamie and held on to her in terror, all three heads began to cry out in unison:

"The evil lives! The evil lives!"

TO BE CONTINUED

in FEAR STREET NIGHTS #3:
DARKEST DAWN

About the Author

R.L. Stine invented the teen horror genre with Fear Street, the bestselling teen horror series of all time. He also changed the face of children's publishing with the mega-successful Goosebumps series, which *Guinness World Records* cites as the Best-Selling Children's Books ever, and went on to become a worldwide multimedia phenomenon. The first two books in his new series Mostly Ghostly, *Who Let the Ghosts Out?* and *Have You Met My Ghoulfriend?* are *New York Times* bestsellers. He's thrilled to be writing for teens again in the brand-new Fear Street Nights books.

R.L. Stine has received numerous awards of recognition, including several Nickelodeon Kids' Choice Awards and Disney Adventures Kids' Choice Awards, and he has been selected by kids as one of their favorite authors in the National Education Association Read Across America. He lives in New York City with his wife, Jane, and their dog, Nadine.

Here's a sneak peek at

FEAR STREET NIGHTS #3:
DARKEST DAWN

The evil isn't dead yet. . . .

Both girls were screaming now, screaming and crying, and frantically pulling at their hair.

They probably wouldn't make it to the dance.

I decided it was time for me to leave. I raised my wings and took off, floating high above Jamie's house.

They still hadn't seen me. If they had, they would have screamed some more. They would have recognized me, the blackbird with one eye missing.

And they would know that the EVIL lives, the evil still haunts them.

At least, they consider me evil. I have a different point of view. I think I'm on the side of justice. I only want what is fair.

After all, they invaded my house last year. They broke into the Fear Mansion and looted it. They gleefully stole our possessions.

Didn't anyone ever teach these kids that crime doesn't pay?

Well, that's what I plan to do. I plan to teach them that important lesson.

Dana and Jamie think they have killed the evil. Burned it in that fiery kiln in Jamie's garage. They think they can relax now.

But I'm still here.

I'm closer to them than ever.

And I have the amulet. The jeweled pendant that gives me so much power.

They won't get away with their crime. I'll see to that.

I'm not evil. What an ugly word that is. I desire only *justice*.

Trying to burn us away gives me even more reason to seek my revenge.

Even more reason to kill them one by one.

FEAR STREET®—

WHERE YOUR WORST NIGHTMARES LIVE

ALL-NIGHT PARTY

THE CONFESSION

THE PERFECT DATE

KILLER'S KISS

THE RICH GIRL

THE STEPSISTER

By bestselling author

R.L. STINE

Simon Pulse
Published by Simon & Schuster
FEAR STREET is a registered trademark of Parachute Press, Inc.

Britney is the girl everyone
loves to hate.

killing britney

SEAN OLIN

She's **popular, blond,** and **fabulous.**
Sure, people are jealous. . . .

But jealous enough to **want her dead?**

killing britney

A thrilling new novel by Sean Olin

from Simon Pulse • published by Simon & Schuster